The Best of Joe Weider's

MUSCLE & FITNESS

More Bodybuilding Nutrition and Training Programs

The Best of Joe Weider's

MUSCLE
&FITNESS

More
Bodybuilding Nutrition
and Training Programs

Contemporary Books, Inc.
Chicago

Library of Congress Cataloging in Publication Data

Main entry under title:

More bodybuilding nutrition and training programs.

   (The Best of Joe Weider's Muscle & fitness)
   1. Bodybuilders—Nutrition.   2. Bodybuilding.
I. Weider, Joe.   II. Muscle & fitness.   III. Series.
TX361.B64M67   1982   646.7′5   82-45421
ISBN 0-8092-5595-2
ISBN 0-8092-5619-3 (pbk.)

All photos courtesy of the IFBB.

Published by Contemporary Books, Inc.
180 North Michigan Avenue, Chicago, Illinois 60601
Manufactured in the United States of America
Library of Congress Catalog Card Number: 82-45421
International Standard Book Number: 0-8092-5595-3 (cloth)
                              0-8092-5619-3 (paper)

Published simultaneously in Canada by
Beaverbooks, Ltd.
150 Lesmill Road
Don Mills, Ontario M3B 2T5
Canada

Contents

The Best of Joe Weider's

MUSCLE
& FITNESS

More
Bodybuilding Nutrition
and Training Programs

Introduction: The Value of Muscle

by Joe Weider

Controversy has always existed over the way bodybuilding with weights affects the body. The attitude sports coaches once had about weight training is still clear in my mind. They were sure that bodybuilding made you muscle-bound.

At the time, we were struggling to get across our ideas and beliefs about weight training. We knew that among us bodybuilders there were superb weight-trained athletes capable of outstanding performances in conventional sports. But these people preferred to be known simply as bodybuilders.

The point is, bodybuilding develops a lot more than muscle. We preach a lot about muscle size, shape, proportion, definition, and so on, but we know that under the skin there's much more going on physiologically and psychologically. With the ebullience of good health and physical strength comes self-esteem and the ability to cope with adversity.

All is not vanity in bodybuilding. I have always brought muscles to your attention because they represent the true condition of your body. Exercise increases the blood supply to the muscle, enhances the ability of the muscle to extract oxygen and exchange waste products for nutrients, and raises the level of enzymes that control metabolism in the muscle cell. Exercise increases your strength and endurance, your physical capacity for work.

Any kind of exercise, whether bodybuilding, running, cycling, or swimming, primarily trains and conditions the muscles. All the other body organs serve as aids in arriving at your muscular potential. Performance improvement occurs as the results of circulatory and metabolic changes at the level of the muscle cells. Life itself depends on our capacity to do physical work, so strength and endurance are paramount.

From the emphasis on cardiopulmonary fitness these days, you might suspect that the major effect of training is on the heart and lungs. "Guess again," says famous cardiologist George Sheehan, M.D., a runner who has written several popular running books. "Exercise does virtually nothing for the lungs; that has been amply proved by pulmonary specialists. Nor does it especially benefit your heart. Running, no matter what you have been told, primarily trains and conditions the muscles. Leg muscles can improve

as much as 300% in work capacity with minimal changes in heart capability."

According to Sheehan, cardiac rehabilitation is mainly muscle rehabilitation. He maintains that heart patients really conquer fatigue by developing great legs, rather than a great heart. Canadian cardiologist Gordon Cumming writes: "The peripheral circulation regulation and the improvement in the metabolic processes in the muscle can account for the improvement in endurance performance in the absence of an increase in heart stroke volume."

Sheehan, a physician for almost 40 years and a runner for 17, now believes that fitness programs have to do with skeletal muscle rather than heart muscle. "All you need to embark on a fitness program is a potentially trainable pair of legs or arms and a reasonable expectation of increasing your energy and eliminating fatigue."

The late cardiologist Paul Dudley White, himself a dedicated bicyclist, customarily examined his patients' legs. If they were well-muscled and toned, he considered the person a decent surgical risk.

Muscle & Fitness magazine has been in the forefront of health, fitness and strength development. We bodybuilders have always known more than the medical experts about training the body. Experience has given us a vast log of knowledge over the years.

That is why we call our magazine "Muscle *and* Fitness." We know that muscle establishes the base for a powerful, vigorous body. If you want to improve your overall fitness, you have to go in for strength training with intensity. When you are strong and fit, your body fully utilizes the nutrition you give it.

The strength you get from bodybuilding can be retained late in age. We intend to prove this in an upcoming issue devoted to fitness and aging. There are many bodybuilders in their 50s—and some even in their 60s—who look and feel as good as ever.

Women bodybuilders provide another example. Many of them trained for years, out of the limelight, in a field largely dominated by men. Now, too, as they go into their middle years, they have defied aging. The continued improvement they have made in their bodies is phenomenal.

Muscles are a tremendous asset. They give you the ability to withstand fatigue, to handle stress, and they help you get the most out of your life. We observed an ancient tenet in bodybuilding that said: "Train for shape, and strength will follow." Today, backed by research and experience, we can safely say: "Train for muscle, and have the world at your feet."

BODYBUILDING NUTRITION

Is This the Ultimate Muscle-Building Diet?

by Joe Weider

When young bodybuilders come up to me in the gym and ask me about gaining weight, I have a question for them:

"Do you want increased body weight or size?"
Invariably the answer is "Size!"

That should also be your answer because you should never confuse body weight with muscle growth. Just adding more body weight will not produce the razor-sharp definition you must have to be successful. How much do you think an extra inch on your arm will add to the scale? Not much. Muscle, not weight, is the name of the game.

The champion bodybuilders know this, but sometimes it has taken them years to acquire the body wisdom to achieve it. Too many years.

In this article, I will let you in on the nutritional secrets that will spare you those lost years. I will explain how the possession of a few simple facts—and persistent determination—will shorten your journey to the top. I will also explain why beginning bodybuilders should be satisfied with an 8–10 pound yearly gain, and why top bodybuilders are often content with a solid 5-pound gain.

In this article, I will draw on my 45 years of experience in bodybuilding and tell you exactly:

- How to build muscle nutritionally without gaining fat.
- How to plan a daily menu that produces results (I've included a Joe Weider special).
- How to supplement your diet to really make a difference.

Let's consider some basic facts:

Fact #1: Extra body weight, gained too quickly, will result in a loss of definition. How do you know if you're gaining too quickly? Check carefully for excess size in your waist, hips, and the small of the back. The champs have learned after many years that this is where they will first begin to add fat and lose their symmetry.

Fact #2: Body fat is different from muscle. Your body fat is what insulates you from temperature changes. It also helps preserve body heat. The layers of fat in your body round out your body contours. Not only does body fat not add definition, it can prevent it.

3

Statue: Louis Cyr, 19th-Century French-Canadian strongman.

Muscle is what builds definition, and muscle is built by protein. Protein is a *structural* material. It provides the structure of our connective tissues, our tendons, our muscles. Protein not only builds muscle, it builds the fibrous sheets that hold muscles in place. That's definition! To get that definition, you *must* put protein into your diet.

Fact #3: A champion bodybuilder must learn how and when to eat protein. Why? Research indicates that only about 30 grams of protein can be absorbed every 3.5 hours. In other words, the cells cannot be force-fed. How do the champs apply this knowledge? By spacing their meals: eating five or six small meals each day, with 30 grams of protein at each meal. Muscle size—not fat—grows dynamically on this program.

Fact #4: Our body tissues must have nitrogen for growth. Protein is our main source of nitrogen, and it has been found that nitrogen levels in the cells begin to decrease about six hours after meals. If we go too long between meals the cells may fall into nitrogen imbalance, interfering with growth.

How much nitrogen do we need? Biochemically, tissues require about one gram of this element every 3–3.5 hours to maintain a balanced condition of nitrogen. It takes approximately 20 grams of nitrogen to supply this one-gram balance. Spread over five or six meals this translates into 100 grams of protein per day.

But your muscles need more! According to clinical studies, 2–2.5 grams of nitrogen are required to add 25 pounds onto a 70 kilogram man (154 lbs.). This translates into a bodybuilding need of 50 additional grams, or a total of 150 grams of protein per day. With five or six spaced feedings, we arrive at the 30 grams of protein per meal.

Looking for a bodybuilding edge in your meal-spacing system? Try tablets that provide all eight of the essential amino acids. With these you will get readily usable high-quality protein without bloating and fat. In the Weider Olympian line of products, the Dynamic Body Building Blocks are designed exactly for this bodybuilding purpose.

Fact #5: The next question that usually arises is: What type of protein is best?

Animal protein is structurally most like human protein and thus is most easily converted into your muscle. (Proteins are composed of building blocks called amino acids, and it is the structure of the amino acid patterns that is crucial.) H. C. Sherman, Ph.D., M.D., on the Johns Hopkins University faculty, has found that eggs are the most valuable protein for human nutrition. Milk comes next. Tissue protein is third. This protein value is based on its biological activity, that is, how well it is absorbed and how efficiently it maintains and repairs tissues.

What should you do if you find you're starting to gain weight too fast? Many of the champs use a milk-and-egg protein powder mixed in nonfat milk to replace a meal or two daily. This is also a convenient way to get concentrated protein—*without fat and overloading.*

Here's a chart of some basic foods a bodybuilder should and shouldn't be eating:

Good

1. Eggs
2. Nonfat milk
3. Meats
   lean meat
   fish
   fowl (remove skin)
   liver
4. Cheese

Bad

1. *Fatty foods:* which slow the digestive system, create bloating and overload, interfere with digestion and metabolism. Fats have twice as many calories as proteins and carbohydrates. Excess calories mean unwanted body fat.
2. *Refined junk foods:* vitamins and other vital nutrients are removed in the refining. This robs your body of nutrients such as the B vitamins, which are needed for energy and needed to properly metabolize your food.

For at least three important reasons, I am a strong believer in milk and egg protein, including milk-and-egg protein powders:

1. Milk and eggs have the highest biological value of all protein foods.
2. Milk products contain the anterior pituitary hormone secreted by the cow when lactating. The hormone is designed to accelerate the growth of her calf. When humans consume cow's milk, they also can benefit from this growth hormone.
3. Cow's milk contains four times as much *lysine* as human milk. Lysine is an essential amino acid necessary for growth.

Would you like another competitive edge shared by the champions? Try certified raw milk. It's available in many states, in regular, lowfat and nonfat. I believe it is superior to pasteurized milk because the enzymes that are naturally in milk are not destroyed as they are in pasteurization. Pasteurized milk is usually exposed to temperatures of 142–145°F. for 30 minutes. This heat not only kills bacteria, but enzymes, too.

Following is a daily menu designed specifically for champion bodybuilders. It's built on the dynamic nutritional facts I've been explaining. It can work for you, too.

Breakfast: Joe Weider's Special Protein Drink

> 12 oz. half and half
> 2 egg yolks
> 2 tablespoons milk & egg protein
> 1 oz. liquid amino acids
> —Mix in blender for 15 seconds.
> sip slowly.

Special supplements to be used with this drink (to be taken after drink is finished):

> 1 essential amino acid tablet
> 3–4 hydrochloric acid tablets (HCL)
> 3–4 enzyme tablets
> 1 ribonucleic acid tablet (RNA)
> 1 organic iron tablet
> 3 tri-germ oil capsules (essential fatty acids)

Lunch:

> ground beef patty and cottage cheese

> Supplements with lunch:
> same as with breakfast, but omit the iron and the RNA tablets and add one high-potency B-complex tablet

3:00 p.m. snack:

> natural cheese (not processed)
> 1 oz. liquid amino acids

Dinner:

steak or ground beef (up to 1 lb.)
cottage cheese
small mixed green salad with tomatoes

Supplements with dinner:
same as with other two meals, but omit iron
   and add 4 calcium tablets

Before retiring (one hour before bedtime):

protein drink (same as at breakfast)
2 calcium tablets

Between meals (every three hours):

6 liver tablets
1 high-potency B-complex tablet

This bodybuilding menu will give you your protein—at the right time—and it will build your muscles. But don't stop here. Like the champs, you must learn specific ways to burn your body fat to achieve razor-sharp definition. How& With "lipotropics," fat-oxidizing nutrients such as the B-vitamins choline and inositol, which help to regulate your metabolism. The champion bodybuilders usually add lipotropics to their diet at each meal during the last stages of contest preparation. If plagued with excess weight, they'll use them sooner and more often.

Supplements fit perfectly into a program of spaced meals because they require no preparation and can be taken any time. As the champs have learned, proper supplementation can give you the edge you need to build muscle mass—without the fat.

Why Diets Fail

by Armand Tanny

A strange dichotomy exists in our society, "Slim is in," we are told—yet we are literally implored to overeat. Cosmetic and clothing ads feature the lean body, while supermarket and fast food chain commercials offer the quick trip to Fat City at bargain prices.

During the winter, we can hide inside our parkas. But with the advent of warm weather and its beach and pool parties, we may find ourselves bulging out of our clothes and giving the mirror a wide berth. We pounce on the latest fad diet, hoping that the pounds that went on slowly during the winter months will vanish quickly under the influence of the good doctor's "no-strain–no-pain, crash-diet program."

Our calorie-counting world is ruled by two monarchs. They're known as Diet and Exercise. Diet decrees that we give up our fattening lifestyle, which we are loathe to do. Exercise lays down a 10K run to burn off the calories from a surreptitious piece of pie a la mode, a dismaying effort indeed. But we accept the misery of changing our eating habits and prodding a reluctant metabolism into activity. The delicious indulgences we relinquish for an in-shape body somewhere in the distant future takes personal sacrifice beyond the call of duty.

All this is not as grim as it might sound, however. Bodybuilding itself is holistic. It requires training, rest, recuperation, peace of mind, and diet. The end product is health and a conditioned body. Without the proper diet we cannot realize our full potential. We develop a lifestyle to achieve a goal, and diet is part of it.

The fad diet, however, offers no miracle cure for obesity. All diets work at first, but inevitably we return to the gastronomic folly of our old ways. Over a two-year period all diets fail because they are not designed with a lifestyle such as bodybuilding in mind.

The word *"diet"* is an abomination. To change a fat-producing fare to a more natural and wholesome one, we must make a change in our eating habits to complement our lifestyle. And what better lifestyle than holistic bodybuilding!

First of all, we need the willpower to resist the promises in the seemingly tireless proliferation of fad diets. The cure lies within us. We don't need the help of weight-loss gurus. We do need the personal awareness that our weight has slipped

7

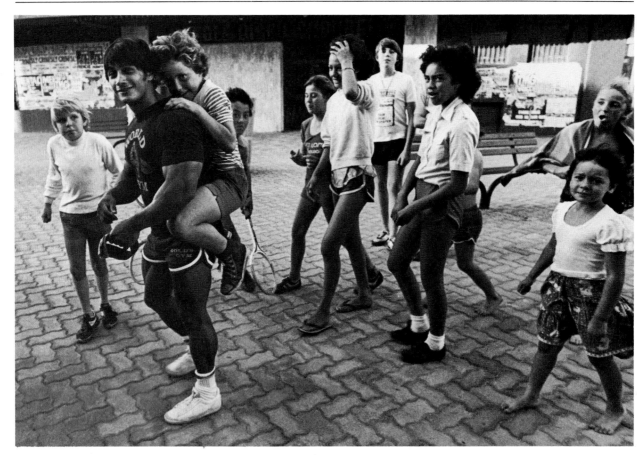

out of bounds. Next, we need some kind of motivation that permits us to make corrections. In addition, we need an inner strength, the ability to give up old self-defeating ways and to construct rewarding patterns of eating and living.

We may have been using food as a crutch or a way of coping with life. When life disappoints us, we turn to food for solace. Now we must initiate a dependency shift. Instead of looking to food to solve our problems of boredom, anxiety, and frustration, we must turn to more realistic ways by confronting troublesome situations head-on. We must learn to cope, to replace the knife-and-fork solution by reeducating ourselves in the basics of healthy eating habits.

Finally, we must learn to deal with relapses. New research shows that people are able to diet comfortably for 24 hours. Conventional dieting—in which the dieter never gets a break—is actually counterproductive for many overweight

persons. Prolonged dieting triggers the body's survival mechanisms, causing calories to burn more slowly, thus letting the body maintain its weight despite the lowered intake of food.

If we slip from a sensible diet one day, it affects only that day. We are allowed a fresh start the next day. This is far less stressful since we don't feel so terribly deprived. We can maintain a more normal social life as well, if we feel more comfortable with this off again–on again eating regimen, we might well be encouraged to stay with it over a longer period.

A reduced-calorie plan should have a variety of foods scientifically programmed to produce a high level of fat burn-off. By their temporary nature, diets were never intended to succeed. Only if we learn to live a healthy life do we have a real chance of losing weight and keeping it off. We need the help of exercise, and one of the best bets is holistic bodybuilding.

Nutrition and the Ultimate Body

by Joe Weider

"Experience is the best teacher."

For the bodybuilder attempting to increase muscle size and density while trying to achieve razor-sharp definition, that axiom leaves much to be desired. The bodybuilding greats of old took years to learn how to read their bodies and to understand the effects of nutrition on their muscular structure. Many aspirants never learned. They either ate too much or too little.

Told that protein was the most vital nutrient, many bodybuilders overdosed, and their bodies suffered. Some confused bulk with muscle, and took a shortcut to obesity. Through a process of trial and error, many got to the top. In fact, the reigning crop of professional bodybuilders come from the trial-and-error school.

By following a few simple rules and being persistent, however, you can shorten the distance to the top by at least 30%. Some people today are reaching that level in half the usual time. All it takes is some knowledge of biochemistry and an awareness of standard training principles.

In the old days some hard-training bodybuilders would eat several pounds of meat a day. But now we know that muscle cells cannot be force-fed. It has been learned that the practice of eating small but frequent meals promotes more efficient muscle growth than eating the usual three meals a day.

NITROGEN BALANCE

A careful consideration of the quality of the diet and the spacing of meals is critical to success.

Protein heads the list of vital nutrients. Protein contains nitrogen, which muscle cells require.

It has been found that nitrogen levels in cells begin to decrease about 4–5 hours after eating. If we go too long between meals, the cells may fall into imbalance even though the blood may continue to show positive nitrogen levels.

Biochemically, in order for tissue to maintain a balanced condition of nitrogen, a feeding of about 3–3.5 grams of nitrogen every 3–3.5 hours is required. It takes about 6.5 grams of protein to fulfill this requirement. These findings indicate that, to maintain this balance, the average person must take in about 100 grams of protein a day.

MUSCLE GROWTH

When you're training, however, you need more than maintenance nitrogen in order to build muscle. Clinical studies have shown it takes about 50 additional grams of protein daily to promote muscle growth. So the bodybuilder in training requires a total of 150 grams of protein a day.

ABSORPTION

What is the best way to utilize 150 grams of protein daily? Research has shown that only about 30 grams can be absorbed every 3.5 hours. So by eating five or six small meals daily, each meal supplying 30 grams of protein, you can achieve maximum muscle growth.

Bodybuilding workouts are said to tear down muscle cells, and the body's compensation for this results in muscle growth. Actually, the muscle cells do not tear down in the literal sense, but specific amino acids supplied by protein are rapidly stripped of their nitrogen. If a constant supply of protein is being provided, the cells respond to the demand that bodybuilding training places on them and slowly increase in size. Thus the bodybuilder who eats his total daily protein requirement in just two or three meals simply overloads his system and fails to extract the maximum benefit from his food.

BEST PROTEINS FOR MUSCLE GAINS

Protein value is based on its biological activity—i.e., how well it is absorbed, and how efficiently it maintains and repairs tissues. H. C. Sherman, Ph.D. and M.D., Johns Hopkins University, found that eggs are the most valuable protein for human nutrition. Next is milk and milk products.

Each meal should include one of the following: meat, fish, fowl, cheese and/or eggs. The bodybuilder with a busy daily schedule may find it convenient to use a milk-and-egg protein

Food Combining for the Bodybuilder

by Charles Fraser

Many bodybuilders wonder why they're not always full of energy and enthusiasm for training when they arrive at the gym. Many wonder why they have plateaus or even slumps in their muscle-building progress. It may be because they are tired from inefficient digestion resulting from poor food combinations. No matter how much, or how wholesome, the food you eat, you cannot build muscle tissue and strength if that food is not properly digested and assimilated!

Of course, hard, intelligent training is also necessary for building muscle. No one ever developed a great physique without exercise. But nutrition is at least 50% of the battle.

A slogan heard for decades is that "we are what we eat." But it ain't necessarily so. My contention is: Far more important that what we eat is *what we digest and assimilate*. Put another way, the foods that we select to eat are not as important as the combinations in which we eat them, because these combinations determine how well we digest the foods.

To survive as they spread over the earth, humans learned to eat a great variety of foods, including different animal meats and products.

Consequently, they drew apart from their natural instincts and simple eating habits. Civilized humans found themselves eating an enormous variety of foods in helter-skelter combinations. Modern humans now suffer from inferior health, with weakened physiques and lack of vigor. Compared to our pristine ancestors, we are powder puffs. Yet, how many of us ever question our eating habits?

Consider these points. Humans are the only animals that:
- Eat cooked food.
- Eat food parts, or extracts.
- Eat a variety of foods at one sitting.
- Drink liquids before, during, and after meals.
- Eat refined, processed, and denatured foods.
- Eat foods incompatible with their physiology.
- Consume stimulants, depressants, and other poisons.

These points, which are discussed at length in the work of the great natural hygienist Herbert M. Shelton, are raised here to encourage the bodybuilder to give serious consideration to the very important subject of combining foods.

First, we must free our minds of erroneous

beliefs about how to eat meals. The "well-balanced meal" is the worst thing you can put in your stomach! Humans, like most animals, are supplied with but one mouth and one stomach. Almost all animals eat only one food at a time, or very simple combinations of two or three foods. When several different foods are swallowed, in rapid succession, the stomach is thrown into a state of confusion about the digestive enzymes required. Under such circumstances, it's lucky that there's *any* digestion whatsoever.

Each animal in nature eats those foods for which it is constitutionally suited. The horse—a graminivorous animal—selects, chews, swallows, digests, and assimilates grasses and grains because its teeth, saliva, digestive capabilities, liver, and intestinal tract naturally lead the horse to find these foods delicious and compatible with his organism.

The carnivore kills and eats its prey because its body and instincts lead it to see other animals as food. The tiger eats meat only. He doesn't have potatoes or coffee with his meal. If there were no other animals, the carnivore would starve in a paradise of fruits and vegetation.

On the other hand, the gorilla, which is closely related to man, eats fruit, celery, and a great quantity of succulent green leaves. He's rarely seen drinking water. There is an exotic bird in South America that apparently eats nothing but bananas.

These examples should suffice to make the point that each animal is constituted to eat food that is best for it. These foods are whole and natural—the type found in Nature.

In presenting the principles of food combining I'm relying on the works of the natural hygienists I've read over a period of 20 years. For those interested in examining the subject more thoroughly, I recommend the books of the aforementioned Herbert M. Shelton. I consider his books, *Food Combining Made Easy, Superior Nutrition,* and volume two of *The Hygienic System* to be the most thorough and erudite works on food and nutrition ever written.

While those who advocate proper food combining recommend a completely vegetarian diet, if you are a meat and animal protein eater, relax!—this article is not intended to persuade you to give up these foods. My intention is to help you get more out of the foods you do eat, which will, in turn, improve the results of your bodybuilding training. In the menus listed later, there will be an effort to introduce readers to a variety of foods which they may prefer over their usual boring diet, including meat.

Because humans are not naturally carnivorous, and must eat a great deal of vegetable food with their meat, the result has been an unfortunate marriage of carbohydrates and proteins in the same meal. This is the greatest cause of digestive havoc ever known. Meat, cheese, and eggs eaten in combination with bread, grains, pasta, potatoes, rice, beans, cereals, and other carbohydrates usually form the traditional dish of every civilized people in the world. This habit is so ingrained, people accept these combinations as if they naturally go together.

Who would eat pizza by having the cheese in one meal and the crust in the next? Who would eat eggs without toast or fried potatoes? What Chinese food buff would eat his chop suey without the bed of rice? Who would pick the potatoes out of the Irish beef stew?

Yet all these dishes are extremely incompatible food combinations. The digestive labor required of human stomachs, no matter how "accustomed" they are to these dishes, is truly heroic. And the digestion saps the body of energy that could be used for bodybuilding workouts and growth.

Why is this so? The human mouth begins to secrete the enzyme *ptyalin* in the saliva as soon as any carbohydrate is taken in and chewed. This is the beginning of carbohydrate digestion. The mouth sends a signal to the stomach that a carbohydrate is on the way. The stomach begins secreting digestive juices in the form of enzymes to handle the carbohydrate. If a protein food comes into the stomach almost at the same time, the digestive juices necessary for its digestion are inhibited and weakened by the carbohydrate digestion that has already begun. So the protein sits there, spoiling and fermenting as the beleaguered food bag tries to carry out its now more difficult task of cabohydrate digestion. Then, perhaps hours later, the stomach will attempt to take care of the digestion of the protein—but now with the energy-drain handicap of having to deal with the spoilage and fermentation. This explains why people on a conventional diet experience burping and later on, when the food has been moved to the lower intestine, flatulence. Is there any wonder why the person on a conventional diet is apt to feel sluggish all day?

General Nutrition Rules

1. Eat proteins and carbohydrates at separate meals.
2. Eat only one concentrated protein at a meal.
3. Eat acids and starches at separate meals.
4. Eat acid fruits separately from sweet fruits.
5. Eat proteins and acids at separate meals.
6. Eat fat and proteins at separate meals.
7. Eat sugars and proteins at separate meals.
8. Eat melons alone.
9. Drink milk alone, or leave it out of your diet.
10. Never take liquids with a meal or shortly afterward.

On page 18, there is a suggested menu taken from Shelton's *Superior Nutrition* and modified to suit the diet of those who want to eat meat and animal products. First, let me explain the salads listed here. They should be very large, at least three or four times the size of those "token salads" you receive with a meal in a restaurant. The salad should consist mostly of green, leafy vegetables. Do not limit yourself to bleached out head lettuce. Consider all these: romaine, Bibb, Boston, butter. Also use escarole, spinach, chard, parsley, watercress, dandelion greens, collard greens, cabbage, celery, and broccoli. Some of these greens have a strong and slightly bitter taste, but mixed with other greens, and with cucumber, tomato, or bell pepper (red or green) added, they can become highly palatable.

These greens are extremely rich in all or most of the minerals. Minerals are the great creators of the body. They are essential for the utilization of everything else: fats, carbohydrates, proteins, and vitamins. Greens are also high in vitamins A and E and contain quality amino acids. The collard is the richest green in minerals, and also contains an amazing 6–7% protein.

SUGGESTED MENU

FOR SPRING AND SUMMER

	Breakfast	Lunch	Supper
MONDAY	Cherries Plums Apricots Cottage Cheese	Vegetable Salad Steamed Spinach Fresh Corn Carrots	Vegetable Salad Okra Raw Cashews
TUESDAY	Grapefruit	Vegetable Salad Steamed Turnips Baked Beans	Vegetable Salad Squash (Zucchini) Sunflower Seeds
WEDNESDAY	Watermelon	Vegetable Salad Broccoli Asparagus Sweet Potatoes	Vegetable Salad Squash Corn Lamb Chop
THURSDAY	Nectarines Cherries Banana Cottage Cheese	Vegetable Salad Spinach Carrots Cauliflower	Vegetable Salad Steamed Collard Greens Celery Ground Beef
FRIDAY	Melon	Peaches Plums Apricots (a light lunch)	Vegetable Salad Green Beans Avocado (a light-medium supper)
SATURDAY	Watermelon	Vegetable Salad Yellow Squash Spinach Broiled Fish	Cherries Nectarines Bananas (a light supper)

FOR FALL AND WINTER

MONDAY	Persimmons Grapes Apple	Vegetable Salad Steamed Collard Greens Soft- or Hard-Boiled Eggs	Vegetable Salad with Avocado Broccoli Roast Beef or Pork
TUESDAY	Pear Apple Grapes	Vegetable Salad Chinese Cabbage String Beans Steamed Squash	Vegetable Salad Spinach Steamed Beets Pecans
WEDNESDAY	Grapes Apple Figs	Vegetable Salad Spinach Raw Fish (Sashimi)	Vegetable Salad Steamed Collard Greens Filberts (Hazelnuts)
THURSDAY	Oranges Grapefruit	Vegetable Salad Cauliflower Spinach Steamed Potatoes	Vegetable Salad Steamed Eggplant Steamed Eggplant Walnuts
FRIDAY	Oranges	Vegetable Salad Kohlrabi Turnip Greens Peanuts	Vegetable Salad Okra Yellow Wax Beans Chicken (steamed or broiled)
SATURDAY	Dates Bananas	Vegetable Salad Okra Squash Baked Potato	Vegetable Salad Asparagus Eggplant (baked) Brazil Nuts

In making the salad, I suggest you break or cut the vegetables into large pieces. Eat the salad without dressing if possible. But if you must have a dressing, try a little vegetable oil and lemon. Those vegetables which are cooked should be steamed in as little water as possible and removed from the pot while they are still firm.

All fruits should be eaten raw, of course.

The suggested menus contain foods that are generally well combined, although some of the vegetables included in the protein meals are mild carbohydrates. It is best, therefore, to eat these foods sequentially, so that the protein is eaten last.

Liquids should not be drunk during or immediately after a meal. Liquids dilute both the food swallowed and the digestive juices. Liquids can be taken 10 minutes before a meal, 30 minutes after a fruit meal, an hour or more after a carbohydrate meal, and two hours or more after a protein meal. Drink only when thirsty and only enough to satisfy thirst.

Never consume table salt. Salt is inorganic material dug out of the ground. It cannot be used by the body for either energy or building tissue. Humans are not plants. Only plants can assimilate mineral (earth) materials directly. Salt becomes soluble in the body, but is eventually excreted wholly unchanged and unused. While it is in the body, it is treated by the organism as a poison—which it is! Salt adversely affects definition and muscle density. At a body weight of 200 pounds, a salt eater will carry 7–10 pounds of detrimental water weight. The bodybuilder who quits eating salt will lose all that water in 7–10 days without losing one ounce of muscle.

The eating principles presented here lead to increased digestive and assimilative efficiency. So by following them, the bodybuilder will be able to eat less food and yet maintain his or her body weight. Bodybuilders who adopt these eating principles will have more energy and endurance for training. They will be able to develop muscle faster and more healthfully. Anyone who gives food combining a fair trial will be delighted with the results—both in bodybuilding and in health.

Diet Tips for the Bodybuilder

by Arnold Schwarzenegger

The better the nutrition, the better an athlete is able to perform. The relationship between food and performance has been known for a long time. Wrestlers in ancient Greece ate bull testicles to give them strength and muscle. The ancients had no scientific backing for diets, but they knew that what they ate gave them the energy needed for top performance.

Today's fitness revolution has caused us to take a hard look at basic nutrition. When athletes win, they tend to credit the sequence of events preceding the contest. They feel that if the routine worked once, it will work again. Although they don't know why a particular food helped them win, if deprived of this food while training for a subsequent event, they often do not fare as well. At the Olympics, athletes from different nations are fed the same diet they had in their homeland. The breaststroker from Japan will fare better on fish and rice than on the meat-and-potato diet of the American swimmer.

Aside from the psychological benefit of a certain food or combination of foods, the best diet known for the athlete contains 20% protein, 35% fat, and 45% carbohydrate. It so happens that these proportions are essentially what the average American eats every day.

ENERGY NEEDS

From the results of carefully controlled studies of intense athletic activity, it is possible to reach these conclusions on energy requirements:

- Energy for exercise is derived from fats and carbohydrates. Whether fats or carbohydrates are used depends on the amount of oxygen available to the muscle. When the training is aerobic, as in distance running, and plenty of oxygen is present, fats are used. With heavier, high-speed work like weightlifting and sprinting, carbohydrate is the primary source of energy.
- Protein is not used as an energy source during exercise.
- The ability to perform heavy, prolonged exercise is greater when the stored muscle glycogen level is high.
- When glycogen stores are depleted, work decreases.
- Glycogen stores can be increased through "carbohydrate loading."

THE CONTROLLED DIET

Runners have been using the carbohydrate loading method to supercharge the muscles with glycogen. The competitive bodybuilder faces the problem of maintaining a high energy level during countdown contest training, while keeping a high degree of muscular definition. The low carbohydrate diet has been the rule in bodybuilding competition training. As a result, the athlete often enters the contest depleted of energy and with muscles "flattened out" by water retention.

Long, hard running and contest bodybuilding training have much in common. They both require much carbohydrate energy. A runner who has just completed a Saturday training run, and has completely exhausted the supply of glycogen in his muscles, must restore the energy if he wishes to run at full capacity the following Saturday.

On a seven-day basis, the diet on Sunday, Monday, and Tuesday should consist of fat and protein only to keep the glycogen in the muscles low. Sunday should be a light workout day, followed by two days of greatly increased training intensity to fully deplete the muscle glycogen. On Wednesday, Thursday, and Friday the athlete's diet should be as much as 70% carbohydrate. Training on Wednesday should be moderate, decreasing even further in intensity on Thursday and Friday. The body tends to

overcompensate by laying in an additional store of glycogen—above the level of the previous week. Recent studies on runners indicate that an increase of as much as 50% in glycogen can be accomplished. The benefits seem evident. The drawbacks, if any, are yet to be determined.

Some top bodybuilders have recently tried carbohydrate loading before a contest. Bodybuilding veterans ease up on weight training the final week and increase their hours of posing and tensing. Since they are not training as heavily, they don't need as much protein as before; they can also cut back drastically on their fat intake.

On the day of the contest, the athlete may eat whatever he thinks will help him win. The bodybuilder needs to curtail his liquid intake just before the competition, which also means avoiding food with a great deal of liquid content.

Athletes on a low-carb diet must carefully avoid sugar on the day of the contest because the slightest sugar intake causes water retention that could kill muscular definition.

The carbohydrate-rich diet also is very effective at high altitudes. Mountain climbers at altitudes above 8,000 feet showed considerably improved performance during heavy activity on a diet that was close to 70% carbohydrate. In

treadmill tests they had more than double the endurance of a control group on a normal diet. They also showed much less tendency to develop altitude sickness.

Perhaps the oxygen deficiency at high altitude is comparable to the lessened supply of oxygen to the muscle during prolonged, exhausting exercise at sea level. The oxygen-deficient, glycogen-burning muscle functions better when glycogen stores are adequate. At high altitude, the effect of glycogen loading is apparent after only a few minutes of intense activity. At sea level, the benefits are not apparent until much later.

The only apparent drawback to carbohydrate loading is that during the depletion period the heart may be forced to function without glycogen, its main source of energy. Also, a sudden overload of carbohydrate may cause a fluctuation in the heartbeat. Researcher Gabe Mirkin, M.D., reported an isolated incident of this involving a 40-year-old marathoner.

EMPTY STOMACH

In general, the liquid diet on the day of the contest is taboo for the bodybuilder, although for other athletes it may actually be recommended. Most sports medicine doctors generally agree that food of any kind should be eaten no later than three hours before competition. It's doubtful that any kind of food on the contest day will add to the athlete's performance.

BODY WEIGHT

The true *muscular* body weight of the athlete can be ascertained easily by underwater weighing. The lean, wiry long-distance runner and the defined, massively muscled bodybuilder may both have the same relative percentage of fat. You can't go on usual height and weight tables. Each athlete has his specific endeavor and ability. The bodybuilder is not built to run a 2-hour, 10-minute marathon, and the marathoner cannot flex a 20-inch biceps.

Athletic performance, however, is not measured by the lack of body fat. The bodybuilder's ability is measured by the size, shape, proportion, density, and definition of his muscle. The runner's ability is measured in terms of time. The food they eat will help increase their ability.

Eating to Get Big and Cut

by Bill Dobbins

The bodybuilder reached out with both hands and his muscular arms tensed as he raised the heavy weight—in this case, a plate containing his breakfast of six eggs, rice, fruit, sausage, bacon, and rolls.

And he was not the only one gorging himself. Breakfast was provided for the 1980 Mr. Universe competitors in Manila, and the Philippine Plaza Hotel had laid out quite a spread. It was Saturday morning, and the prejudging would begin soon. These bodybuilders had trained hard, and they nearly starved themselves to earn the right to compete here; now, many of them were "carbing up," believing that the extra carbohydrates would give them the energy needed to get through the rigors of the contest.

If competitive athletes tend to be extremists about their diets, bodybuilders verge on the fanatic. To get big, they tend to eat too much, especially protein; to get cut, they nearly starve their bodies of essential nutrients. But the more successful ones, the true champions, have learned to control their weight intelligently—using knowledge and discipline instead of fanaticism.

EATING TO GET BIG

Let's start by looking at what is considered a balanced and nutritious diet for the average person. More than half this diet should contain complex carbohydrates, with the balance consisting of protein (about 20% of the total diet) and fat. A person should eat a variety of foods from each of the food groups (meat, dairy products, grains, vegetables, and fruits) to ensure that the diet provides all the necessary vitamins and minerals. Finally, this diet should include a moderate number of calories.

Surprisingly, the bodybuilder's dietary needs are not all that different than the nonathlete's. There is no magic diet, no special food, that confers extra strength, endurance, or muscle growth. But, because of the strain of training, there are some guidelines that bodybuilders ought to be aware of:

Bodybuilders need more carbohydrate. Carbohydrate provides the major fuel used by the body for energy. Bodybuilders need to eat more complex carbohydrates than nonathletes. These carbohydrates provide the fuel and energy the bodybuilder needs for training. Simple

23

sugars, which provide energy but have no nutritional value, should be kept to a minimum.

Bodybuilders need more protein. When the body is put under a great deal of strain (such as during intense training), the body's protein requirements are increased. The average person needs approximately one gram of protein for each kilogram (2.2 lbs.) of body weight. The bodybuilder needs about one gram for every pound of body weight.

Bodybuilders also need more calories than the average nonathletic person, but not so many calories that the body begins to store them as fat.

THE PREWORKOUT MEAL

It takes 3–4 hours for most food to be digested sufficiently to allow the maximum amount of blood to leave the digestive system and go to the muscles used during strenuous exercise. This digestion time is longer if the meal was high in protein and fat.

Bodybuilders who train in the morning frequently eat fruit before the workout, since their systems are low in glycogen after eight hours or more without food. This is a good idea, because the carbohydrate from the fruit rapidly becomes available for energy. Eating candy or some other sugar-loaded food is not a good practice. Refined sugar draws fluid into the gastrointestinal tract and can cause cramps, nausea, gas, and diarrhea during heavy exercise.

One way to avoid waking up completely depleted of carbohydrates is to eat right before going to bed at night. Despite traditional advice to the contrary, there are two good reasons for doing this: (1) Eating several small meals a day is better than eating fewer big ones; and, (2) A protein meal eaten before going to bed gives the body all night to digest this difficult-to-absorb nutrient. This protein will also give you a higher blood-sugar level when you awaken.

If you plan to train later in the day, remember to leave plenty of time for your food to digest. For example, eating around noon and then training at four o'clock would give you time to digest your meal.

A lot of bodybuilders use vitamin and mineral supplements to boost their energy during workouts. It is a good idea to use supplements to ensure that you have all the vital nutrients you need, but no vitamin or mineral can create energy. These nutrients are simply catalysts that act as part of the process in which food is turned into energy.

One nutrient that's frequently overlooked is water. The bodybuilder's requirement for water may be many times that of the average person. This need may not always reveal itself by an increased sense of thirst. It's best to take sips of water frequently during the day, especially if you are on the Weider Double-Split schedule.

Following these guidelines and eating a well-balanced, varied diet is the best way for any bodybuilder to "get big."

EATING TO GET CUT

"I always tell young bodybuilders," says 1980 Grand Prix overall champion Chris Dickerson, "not to do anything extraordinary to get ready for a contest. Just eat less."

Most bodybuilders agree that reducing body fat for a contest involves dieting for 6–8 weeks before a contest and gradually cutting down your caloric intake as the contest draws near. But too many bodybuilders still equate carbohydrate deprivation with fat loss, and this is a mistake.

In dieting for a contest you should eat as you always do, but eat less. Any extreme, such as too much protein or too little carbohydrate, will prevent your body from operating at peak efficiency.

EATING FOR A CONTEST

In Manila, the bodybuilders who were eating

such a huge precontest breakfast believed they needed plenty of carbohydrate to give their bodies energy for the competition. With the contest only a few hours away, they figured there was no chance the breakfast would make them fat. What they didn't realize was that fat gain was the least of their worries.

When carbohydrate is introduced into the body, the excess is stored in the form of glycogen in the liver and the muscles.

But this storage process takes time. Eating a lot of carbohydrate the day of the contest, or even the night before, does not give the body time to create and store glycogen. In fact, in the short term, carbohydrates raise the blood sugar level and cause the body to retain a lot of subcutaneous water.

"The process of storing glycogen in the muscles takes about three days," Joe Weider advises, "and the bodybuilder should be careful not to overeat during those three days."

SUMMARY

To Get Big

- Eat plenty of carbohydrate and protein, but watch those calories.
- Eat a balanced diet that includes something from every food group.

- Don't eat meals during the three hours before you train; fruit eaten prior to a workout is a good source of energy.
- A protein meal eaten before you go to bed will keep your blood sugar level steady. But be sure you count this meal in your total caloric intake.

To Get Cut

- Eat a balanced diet and simply cut down on your calories.
- Increase your expenditure of calories by doing more aerobic exercise such as running or riding a bicycle.
- Don't expect to lose more than about two pounds of fat a week.
- Keep carbohydrates in the diet, or you will find yourself metabolizing lean body mass.
- Begin a high-carbohydrate diet three days before a contest, but don't overeat.
- Drink plenty of fluids. Excess retention of body water comes more from improper diet than from drinking too much.

CONCLUSION

Individual metabolic rates vary a great deal. Because of this, each bodybuilder must make adjustments in training and diet to suit his or her own needs. This is the basis of the Weider Instinctive Training Principle.

The guidelines offered here are intended as a starting point. It is essential that a bodybuilder learn the fundamentals of good nutrition—and understand his or her own metabolism—before trying a radical diet.

No one set of nutrition rules is going to suit everyone. But these guidelines are based on biochemistry, and not just opinions that bodybuilders circulate around a gym. Used as guidelines, rather than hard and fast rules, they can help prevent damaging and disappointing mistakes in your diet.

Building a Muscular Body in a Junk-Food World

by Joe Gold

Junk food is the nemesis of the bodybuilder. It offers little nourishment to hard-working muscles; it's loaded with fat, sugar, chemicals, and salt; and the caloric content virtually eliminates the possibility of attaining maximum muscular definition.

The harmful effects of highly processed junk food far outweigh its nutritional benefits. Junk food distributors pander to our mania for convenience by skillful and manipulative advertising and ready availability. The hurried pace of life, activities such as television viewing, etc., have made eating junk food a relatively unconscious act. It seems that what we eat has to have a strong effect on our taste buds to counter the powerful distractions around us. This probably explains why we prefer extremely sweet, salty, spicy, greasy foods.

It can be said in praise of the diet fads that they have, at least, alerted us to the harmful effects junk foods have on the body. Through advertising we are implored to eat junk food, yet we are surrounded by official information pointing out the nutritional irrationality of such a diet. This is the ridiculous dichotomy that exists in our society.

Directly attributable to our nutritional habits is the epidemic-level incidence of cancer, cardiovascular disease, high blood pressure, diabetes, and obesity. Salt, or sodium, is added to nearly all processed foods. It's estimated that our consumption of salt is about five times what our bodies actually need. Salt is considered one of the main contributing factors to the development of high blood pressure. Hypertension can start in early childhood and may occur at any age until, in adult life, nearly everyone has it.

Most of us on the average American diet have systolic blood pressure equal to 100 plus our age. When you reach age 60, that means your blood pressure will be 160, which is considered okay according to the formula. But we also know that it's possible for an in-shape, diet-conscious person of 60 to have a blood pressure under 130. High blood pressure does not have to develop with age; it only appears that way due to the average American diet.

Cholesterol is the main constituent of the yellow fatty deposits inside our arteries. These deposits increase in size until they close off blood flow, causing a coronary or a stroke.

27

Cholesterol is present in all animal meats, as well as eggs. We have limited ability to dissolve and expel it, so it accumulates in our bodies. It's even found in the arteries of children who eat junk food. The cholesterol count of the average American ranges from 180 to 300. Ideally, it should be less than 160.

Meat protein is high in fat. Even lean meats may have more than 50% fat; cheese may have up to 80%. Animal fat causes the body to produce cholesterol.

Despite advertising to the contrary, polyunsaturated vegetable fat that has been squeezed out of grains, nuts, or seeds, and has been chemically treated, tends to raise the triglyceride (fat) level in the blood. In fact, it raises it more than animal fat does. The blood cells become sticky, and for several hours, their ability to carry oxygen is impaired. Vegetable fat seems to increase the chance of gallstones and cancer even more than animal fat does.

The danger in refined sugars is well-documented. Refined sugars raise both blood sugar and triglyceride levels. The energy roller-coaster effect such sugars cause can produce serious psychological symptoms.

Fast-food items such as the hot dog and hamburger are nutritional nightmares. They are high in fat, salt, and cholesterol, and low in fiber. The protein is necessary in our diets, but fast foods can lead to an excess intake of nutrients, which may draw minerals out of the bones, cause kidney stones, and lead to easily broken bones later in life.

How can you avoid junk food? Stock up on raw vegetables and fruits. Raw trail mix consisting of nuts, seeds, and dried fruit is excellent. So is nonfat hoop cheese and whole grain bread. Try a banana sandwich with raw peanut butter. The junk food dispensaries may offer chicken that's okay if you strip off the skin and excess fat. Salads are safe without the oils.

Think before you decide what to eat. Your best decision is raw food. Cooking processes food and thus lessens its nutritional value. Cooked fish or fowl are the best low-calorie, protein foods.

For the bodybuilder, care in the selection of food is important, if one wants to experience the joy of having a muscular, defined, in-shape body. You can still live safely and happily in a junk-food world.

Nutrition and Immune Function

by Robert H. Gordon, M. Ed.

As science continues to play an ever larger role in the world of sports, many athletes want to scrap old habits in favor of recommendations that are more research-oriented. The area of nutrition is no exception. While athletes were at one time concerned about the need for vitamin supplementation, many are now cutting back because some exercise physiologists maintain that there is no proof that supplementing the diet will improve performance.

New research conducted by Joseph J. Vitale, Sc.D., M.D., at Boston University and Boston City Hospital, however, indicates that the antisupplementation proponents have been barking up the wrong tree. Vitamin supplementation may not improve performance, he says, but it may play a very crucial role in maintaining good health. And that good health is required for optimal, long-term performance. Any hardworking athlete can immediately appreciate the implications of this, recalling how frustrating it was to get sick right before an important contest.

In his work, Dr. Vitale notes that virtually every known nutrient studied has some effect on immune function, immunity implies protection against foreign materials (including cancer cells) which can result in disease. The enzymes responsible for the destruction of pathogens (viruses and bacteria) derive their energy from nutrients. If these nutrients are deficient, then obviously the individual is more susceptible to infection and disease.

Any "insult" to the body depletes various body substances. By an insult, we mean *any* kind of stress; breaking a leg, preparing for an exam, arguing with your boss, or training for a sport.

Bodybuilders present a special situation. Not only do they endure the stresses and strains of repeated high-intensity workouts. but their bodies are additionally taxed by the period of protein synthesis that follows. This is important because research indicates that rapid rates of growth are associated with rapid decline in immune function. In other words, the bodybuilder not only needs some vitamin supplementation to recover from the training, but also some additional bolstering to cover the regrowth if optimal health is to be ensured.

Although most nutrients play some role in

29

protecting the body from disease, certain substances have been identified as having a major influence.

For the average bodybuilder, protein consumption is usually adequate in the off-season; during the competitive season, the need for additional intake is realized, and the demands are met. Contest preparation creates a different situation. In an effort to increase definition, it was once popular to reduce the caloric intake by totally eliminating carbohydrates from the diet while maintaining the protein and fat levels. This practice was subsequently shown to be both unsatisfactory and potentially unhealthy. Many competitors wisely adopted the method of reducing the proportions of all three food groups to create a calorie deficit.

Unfortunately, this practice is a mixed blessing because the need to cut calories can be so severe at times that the protein level becomes inadequate to support the effort of rigorous precontest training. Recent studies show that protein insufficiency can result in a concomitant decrease in disease resistance. A more sensible approach to cutting up would be to maintain the caloric intake to ensure adequate nutrition, while relying on long duration activities to burn the fat.

Folic acid deficiency would be expected to affect the more rapidly dividing cells, since a major biochemical function of the vitamin is related to RNA and DNA synthesis. This means that if you were depleted of folic acid, a protein B-complex, your vitamin synthesis would be hindered and you might not make optimal gains in muscle mass. As alluded to earlier, the enzyme systems involved in effectively killing pathogens require a variety of vitamins and minerals: folic acid is one of them, along with iodine and Vitamin B-6 (pyridoxine).

The need for proper iron levels cannot be overemphasized. Iron deficiency, even of the mild type and without anemia, may render parts of the immune system incompetent.

Vitamin A is another extremely important substance. A deficiency causes changes in the epithelium (the surface membrane of the gastrointestinal tract and throat), resulting in a decreased "barrier" system to the sort of bacteria and viruses that cause colds, flu, and strep throat.

Thiamine needs are increased during periods of heavy exercise, and insufficient Vitamin B-12 will cause depressed tissue growth.

As for Vitamin C, the latest research indicates that massive dosages (one gram or more per day) will not in themselves prevent a cold, but will tend to lessen its duration and severity. This touches on another very important point: the need for optimal nutrition during times of sickness cannot be overemphasized if one is to make the fastest possible recovery.

There have been some exciting discoveries of late concerning Vitamin E. Traditionally thought of as an antioxidant, this substance has additionally been found to stimulate the immune response, prevent bacterial infection, and aid in tumor destruction.

It will be recalled that immunity means not only a good defense against some of the mild viruses and bacteria, but also against cancer cells, too. The implication is that vitamin supplementation helps to maintain the integrity of the immune system on a day-to-day basis, which decreases the ability of a potent carcinogen to assert itself and may prevent a major affliction altogether. Since cancers tend to manifest themselves later in life, it's apparently a case of the short-term affecting the long-term.

Undoubtedly, the topic of nutritional supplementation will continue to evoke mixed responses in the near future. Controversial research, investigating previously explored areas, is being conducted, and the fact that everyone's physiological needs are slightly different always stirs up debate.

At present, however, one statement appears to be accurate: vitamin supplementation may not directly improve your short-term performance in the gym, but by improving immune function, overall health and recuperative ability, it seems to be a critical factor for maximizing your ultimate long-term gains.

Milk and the Bodybuilder

by Armand Tanny

What is the truth about milk and the athlete? Some top performers swear by it; others say it gives them mucous and "cotton mouth," particularly in cold weather. Some can drink it and go right to the gym or track and train with no ill effects; others will get stomach cramps if they train right after drinking milk. For some, the fat in milk is easier to metabolize than the fat in a pork chop. Endurance athletes, especially European cyclists, drink milk right after a race for the lactose, which calms the nerves.

For many years we have been told that milk is the perfect food. Research doesn't support this. Although milk contains all the necessary nutrients, including protein, and is unequalled for the critical growth period of infants, it is deficient in iron, Vitamin D, and copper. The fats in milk are largely triglycerides, and the carbohydrate is lactose, otherwise known as milk sugar. It contains plenty of Vitamin A, but is low in B vitamins, except for riboflavin and pantothenic acid. Its low Vitamin C content is further diminished by pasteurization.

In cow's milk, lactose (the main carbohydrate) makes up about 5% of the total weight. A lactose molecule contains both glucose and galactose. Linked together, they must be split through hydrolysis for your body to digest them. The digestion goes on in the small intestine, facilitated by an enzyme called lactase. Lactase is the enzyme, lactose the food. Unfortunately, not everybody has sufficient lactase to digest all of the lactose present.

Bodybuilders on a bulk-up kick, those who still insist on equating fat with muscle, often complain of gas pains during a workout as a result of excessive milk intake. They drink milk, hoping that the small percentage of protein will all be converted to muscle. Even if it were, the distress would hardly seem worth it.

Lactase deficiency is common in adults. A great part of the world's adult population cannot digest milk easily. It has now been determined that an insufficient supply or a total lack of lactase in the small intestine is the main cause of this deficiency.

For the most part, those who can properly digest lactose come from the cultural groups that have traditionally raised cattle and drunk milk—e.g., Caucasians living in northwestern Europe,

and their American descendants. On the other hand, there is a high lactase deficiency (and, therefore, lactose intolerance) among Orientals, Greek Cypriots, American blacks, Arabs, Ashkenazi Jews, and North American Indians. Almost 100% of the Oriental population is negatively affected by milk.

What is the effect of a lactase deficiency in the intestine? When lactose is not hydrolyzed, it draws water from the large intestine by the process of osmosis. The milk sugar lactose is then fermented by the bacteria in the large intestine. The result is cramps, bloating, and diarrhea—an upleasant condition to contend with during a training season.

Studies have shown that not everyone who is deficient in lactase will experience all or even some of the symptoms. Depending on the amount of enzyme a person can produce, he or she is able to tolerate anywhere from a few ounces to several glasses of milk. The difficulty comes when one exceeds one's limit. The best way to determine the amount of milk you can tolerate, and under what circumstances, is by trial and error.

The lactase deficiency may be hereditary. However, it's not likely to be evident at birth. In the early stage of life, lactase production is at a peak, and it often remains high into childhood. So the deficiency may not show up until adulthood.

Lactase deficiency can be diagnosed in two ways. One is through a lactose tolerance test. A person drinks a quart of milk, then the blood sugar level is measured periodically from blood samples. If the intestine is producing sufficient lactase, the blood sugar will rise. A low blood sugar level means a lactase deficiency.

Another method that can be used is the breath hydrogen test. Exhaled air is collected before and after the ingestion of milk, and the concentration of hydrogen is measured. An increase in the amount of hydrogen indicates a lactase deficiency. (The bacteria in the large intestine is working to break down the milk sugar lactose, and hydrogen is produced.)

You can monitor your own tolerance to milk sugar by keeping a food diary. If there are recurring problems each time you eat milk products or drink milk, the diary provides a valuable record. The next step would be experimenting by cutting down or eliminating foods that contain lactose. When buying foods in a can or box, take a close look at the label to determine whether or not milk or milk products have been added.

Lactose intolerance does not necessarily mean total abstinence from milk products. Cheeses, the unprocessed kind, can be eaten without difficulty. Cheese contains all the milk protein (casein) and butterfat. One-and-a-half ounces of cured cheese contains the nutrients of eight ounces of milk. Well-known Dutch cheeses such as Gouda and Edam contain no lactose after ripening, and some hard English cheeses such as Cheddar and Chesire contain only traces. Processed cheeses should be avoided because of the added coloring agents, preservatives, stabilizers, etc. Only use cheese that's in brick form. It stores better than milk, and usually improves with age.

Yogurt is easily digested because the milk protein has been partially broken down by bacteria. Kefir and buttermilk are more easily tolerated for the same reason. Avoid the flavored supermarket yogurts and the Swiss-style yogurts; stick with the "continental" types that contain active cultures. Most yogurts are made with live cultures, but to ensure longer shelf life, some are heat-treated afterwards. Heat kills the starter bacteria that benefits the person with a lactase deficiency. Look for the quality brands that contain viable cultures. Home-made yogurt should also be started with a quality brand culture.

Supermarkets and drugstores sell enzyme products that can be of help to the lactase-deficient person. These yeast-derived products can be added to plain milk to help break down the lactose. Dairies that pretreat milk with this enzyme will indicate it on the carton.

If you have determined that you have a lactase deficiency and must control your milk intake, it's a good idea to visit a doctor for diagnosis and treatment. You must be sure that nutrients lost

COMPARISON BETWEEN CERTIFIED RAW MILK AND PASTEURIZED MILK

Certified Raw Milk

Will keep for two weeks under constant refrigeration, and will sour normally.

Enzymes: All enzymes available:
Catalase
Peroxidase
Phosphatase
Wulzen Factor (antistiffness)
X-factor in tissue repair

Protein: All 22 amino acids, including the essential eight.

Fats: All 18 fatty acids metabolically available. (Fats are necessary for metabolizing protein and calcium. All natural protein foods contain fats.)

Vitamins: 100% available.

Carbohydrates: Easily utilized in metabolism.

Minerals: 100% metabolically available.

Keeping Qualities: Longer lasting and better tasting.

Pasteurized Milk

Bacteria growth is fast. Turns rancid, not sour.

Enzymes: Less than 10% remaining.

Protein: Lysine and Tyrosine altered by heat. Serious loss of metabolic availability. Less usable protein for growth and tissue repair.

Fats: Altered by heat, especially the 10 essential unsaturated fats.

Vitamins: Unstable, fat-soluble vitamins lost. Up to 80% loss of water-soluble vitamins and more than 50% loss of Vitamin C.

Carbohydrates: Made less available metabolically due to changes caused by heat.

Minerals: 50% loss of calcium due to heat. Loss of enzymes lessens assimilation of needed minerals.

Keeping Qualities: Protective, acid-forming bacteria destroyed. Does not keep well.

---

from incomplete digestion of milk, or from eliminating it entirely, can be replaced by other foods in your diet.

Milk and milk products can be a valuable source of nutrition for the bodybuilder. A glass or two of milk, taken with a protein supplement, can be highly beneficial after a hard workout. The bodybuilder shouldn't categorically reject milk on the grounds that it produces unwanted body fat. The fat in milk offers a good source of energy and, in reasonable amounts, it's fully metabolized during a steady training regimen.

Protein—Your Body's Best Friend

by Ben Weider, C.M.

Proper nutrition is as important as strength and technique in the building of an athletic champion. Every year thousands of spectators are attracted to competitions among renowned athletes. No athlete becomes a champion just through luck or even through natural ability alone. Superior performance requires that all functions of the body operate at peak level.

Performance also is largely affected by what you eat. In early Rome, the gladiators were fed roughly milled grain products to improve their fighting ability. Athletes participating in any sport, especially those engaged in heavy activity such as bodybuilding, depend on careful nutrition. A champion consumes those foods that will give him the best biological support.

Protein, the builder, is considered the most important ingredient in the diet. It cannot perform alone, however. The body also requires fat, carbohydrates, fiber, vitamins, and minerals. These nutrients are successful in their body work only when all are available at the same time and in proportion.

WHY PROTEIN?

A protein molecule is composed of four elements: carbon, hydrogen, oxygen, and nitrogen. Other nutrients found in food are composed of the first three of these elements. But protein requires all four, including nitrogen. The nitrogen atom imparts the building quality to the protein molecule.

Protein is the foundation of every cell in your body. Your skin, hair, nails, enzymes, brain, nervous system, and muscles are protein. The hemoglobin in your blood and the hormones that control your body contain protein. Albumin, a protein, collects fluid wastes from the body for elimination. Without albumin, the body bloats and suffers toxemia. Antibodies, manufactured by the body to combat invading bacteria and other foreign agents, are produced from protein. Protein is even a source of energy. Protein is a strong team made up of strong players.

AMINO ACIDS

The body breaks down the protein in the food you eat and rearranges it into building blocks called amino acids, of which there are a total of 22. Depending on how these amino acids are arranged, different characteristics result. The body can synthesize 14 of the 22. The remaining eight, called the essential amino acids, must be present at each of your meals in sufficient amounts to ensure health.

QUALITY PROTEINS

For the body to build new cells and muscle mass, extra amounts of quality protein must be supplied. When a food contains all eight of the essential amino acids, it's known as a complete protein food. The quality proteins are: meat, fish, poultry, eggs, milk, natural cheese, nuts, and legumes.

Although the protein count in nuts and legumes is high, the amino acid balance is generally lacking. Thus, nuts and legumes should be eaten in combination with other foods that can restore the essential amino acid ratio. The body can use protein only when all the amino acids are present. For example, when supplemented with milk, the low level of methionine (an essential amino acid) in a food such as peanut butter is boosted. The craving for milk when peanut butter is eaten is an example of how nature attempts to restore the balance.

HIERARCHICAL PROTEIN USE

Before you can build muscle tissue, intermediate body functions must be completely satisfied. Energy requirements come first. Natural sugars, starches and fats are the major suppliers of energy. However, for the bodybuilder training at high intensity, additional protein in a meal ensures that the hungry body won't have to start feeding on its own protein for energy. To consume protein for energy, the body extracts and eliminates the nitrogen from it and converts the remaining elements for energy use.

With processed foods it's possible to have a diet low in protein, vitamins, minerals, essential fat, and fiber, but high in calories. The bodybuilder cannot afford this. Additional protein should be available when natural fat and carbohydrate provisions are exhausted.

Researchers have determined that 26 grams of protein maintain blood sugar level in the high energy range for an average of three hours during normal activity. Nutritionists consider this an important clue for growing people. Students, for instance, often go off to school having breakfasted on just cereal and milk—hardly enough to sustain them until their next meal, much less support cell repair or growth. It seems that most adults don't fare much better, even though their bodies require less nutrition due to the slower metabolic rate.

The athlete must be in top condition at the cellular level before he or she can generate additional muscle tissue. Cell activities taking place by the millions every microsecond of your life require continual nutrition. When nutrition is unavailable, cells break down. Rebuilding cells is second in order of importance after the body's energy needs are met. The Food and Nutrition Board of the U.S. National Academy of Sciences has determined that about .41 grams of protein for every pound of body weight will provide daily rebuilding nutrition.

After energy needs and cell repair are satisfied, the body can then use its protein for building new cells and tissue. The body requires twice as much protein for this growth as it does for rebuilding cells. Thus, new cell and tissue creation requires .82 grams of protein per pound of body weight. This requirement is affected by age, weight, genetic profile, digestion and absorption rate, and choice of foods.

Breakfast sets the absorption pattern for the day's other meals. The athlete must maintain a positive nitrogen balance throughout the day. Since extra protein is being supplied for energy use, hunger can be used as a key to the necessary protein intake. Hunger should not occur.

Ben Weider, president of the IFBB, and Dr. Franco Columbu.

On the basis of energy needs, cell repair needs, and cell and tissue growth needs, it is calculated that the 150-pound male athlete needs 123 grams of protein a day. A three-ounce serving of meat, fish or poultry contains 23 grams of protein; an egg and an ounce of cheese both six grams each.

Fruit, grains, and vegetables are important aspects of the balanced meal, for they deliver valuable vitamins, minerals, essential fats, fiber, and carbohydrates.

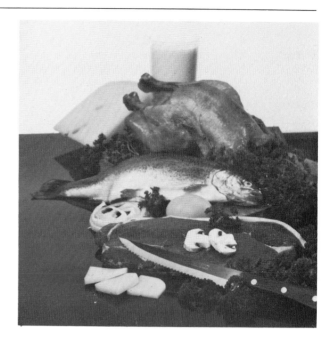

DESIGNING THE MEAL

High-quality protein from a variety of sources assures good protein nutrition. The body requires a range of natural foods. When above-average levels of protein are needed, supplements may be taken. The bodybuilder can develop his individual eating pattern using ways that are right for his taste preference. Some athletes have meat or fish, along with eggs and cheese, at the morning meal. It is a good idea to keep peanut butter available. It's rich in carbohydrates and essential fat. Peanut butter and milk make an excellent protein snack.

Blender drinks have become popular with bodybuilders. These drinks require a minimum of time, fuss, and mess and, with the proper ingredients, can be high in nutrition. A blender drink containing a cup-and-a-half of milk, a banana, two eggs, protein powder, and a few teaspoonfuls of brewer's yeast and carob powder can provide more than 50 grams of protein. The eggs should be put under running hot water to cook them slightly while they're still in the shell; this prevents "egg white injury." Avidin, the raw egg white protein, combines with the B vitamin Biotin in the yolk, preventing assimilation of the nutrients into the bloodstream. Slight cooking deactivates the avidin.

The blender drink above includes four food groups: dairy products; meat, fish, poultry, eggs; fruits and vegetables; and whole grains (the brewer's yeast). You require more than 40 known nutrients and nutritional ratios, which are provided by grouping the foods together in an individual meal.

SUPPLEMENTATION

Those who engage in heavy athletics such as bodybuilding require much higher levels of protein than the average person. Preparing proper quantities of raw food can be discouraging in terms of time and expense. High-quality protein supplements (made with soybean, milk, egg, and meat products) are now available. A big piece of our food dollar is spent for ready-to-eat products or for restaurant meals in which both the quantity and quality of nourishment may be deficient. Air and water pollution increases our nutritional needs to fend off this biological onslaught. More than ever, we need assistance in reaching our nutritional goals. Using protein supplements to meet the needs of the body must be given first priority.

CONCLUSION

The champion bodybuilder is a superior example of health made possible by dedication and know-how. A person can hope to achieve his potential size and optimal state of health only by observing and practicing those principles that develop them.

Modern biochemistry has uncovered important clues, but there is much more yet to be discovered. Athletes and parents of growing children should educate themselves to the unique role of protein foods, along with the teamwork of all the nutrients.

This natural food pattern is not a fad; rather it's the evolution that humankind demands. Energy, enthusiasm, interest, and motivation, as well as physical strength, work, and study, all depend on it.

The Truth about Amino Acids

by Carl Hyland

Probably the two most common comments by bodybuilders are:

"I can't believe what great progress I've made."

And . . .

"I can't believe what lousy progress I've made."

The one element both comments share is surprise. Both results—even the unexpected great progress—indicate that the bodybuilder did not fully understand his or her training. Like a computer, if you know your input, you should know your output.

The major dietary input for most bodybuilders is protein. Protein builds muscle. But what builds protein? The answer is amino acids. Some bodybuilders' poor progress may result from a lack of knowledge about amino acids. Let us address this information deficiency.

And let's begin by telling the end of the story first: the bottom line about amino acids. Basically, animal proteins are better for most bodybuilders than vegetable proteins, but not for the reasons athletes think. Also, any bodybuilder can develop definition with vegetable protein, but only if he or she really understands amino acids.

That's the end. Now let's go back to the beginning.

First, throw out the words "complete" and "incomplete" when talking about protein. They are basically obsolete and confusing. The best way to understand amino acids is to talk about whether they're balanced.

Standard thinking about proteins (and amino acids) goes something like this: animal proteins are "complete" because they contain all the "essential" amino acids. Vegetable proteins are "incomplete" because they don't.

What's the problem with this thinking? The problem is that both animal and vegetable proteins are generally complete.

To understand completeness, you should know about essential amino acids. Protein is composed of 22 amino acids, and all of them must be present for the body to produce protein. It's like an automobile assembly line, if there are no more wheels or engines or brakes to put in the car, you don't have a car—just a collection of parts.

About 14 of these amino acids are easy to get. Even when they're not present in a particular food, the body can make them from various products of metabolism that are normally present. Eight of the amino acids, however, cannot be made by the body in this way, so it's absolutely essential that they are in the diet. These essential amino acids are isoleucine, leucine, lysine, methionine, phenylalanine, threonine, tryptophan, and valine.

Now back to completeness. Animal proteins contain all the amino acids and in a good balance. The confusion comes, however, from the fact that almost all vegetable proteins are also complete. That's right. Most vegetable proteins contain all eight of the essential amino acids, in addition to the nonessentials.

The real problem is balance. Whereas animal proteins contain an ideal balance of the essentials, vegetable proteins do not. Corn, for example, is low in tryptophan. It is complete in that it does have some of this essential amino acid (as well as all the others), but it's not balanced because it doesn't have enough.

To fully understand the implications for the bodybuilder, let's return to the assembly line analogy. Say you want to build 1,000 cars (or 1,000 protein/muscle units). If you have only 500 engines (or 500 tryptophan amino acids), you'll build only 500 cars. Even if you've got 10,000

wheels, 5,000 auto bodies, and 12,300 transmissions, you *will* build 500 cars, but on the 501st, construction will stop. If there's no more tryptophan available in that meal, you might as well shut down the protein plant and go home.

Any amino acid that isn't available in ample supply is referred to as a "limiting" amino acid because when it runs out, it limits the amount of human protein that can be synthesized. This is another useful way to think of proteins.

But what about vegetable proteins? Can this problem of balance be overcome? Yes. You just need to know what you're doing.

Take corn, for example. It's low in tryptophan, but if you combine it with soybeans (which are high in tryptophan), you've got an excellent balance. You've got more than enough to construct your 1,000-unit quota. And the corn also helps the soybeans, which are low in methionine. Corn is high. The two complement one another—thus, the phrase "complementary proteins."

There are, of course, various other considerations. You should know that animal proteins generally are absorbed better than vegetable proteins. It's also true that of the two, vegetable proteins generally contain less fat.

So the next time you hear a bodybuilder commenting on progress, you might ask yourself if he or she really understands amino acids.

Nuts to You

Nuts are the seeds of trees. Trees spread their roots far and deep, drawing minerals from the earth. The leaves of the trees absorb the energy of the sun, as well as rain and air, endowing their seeds with the richest and most concentrated nourishment found in nature. Is it any wonder that as the grandest form of vegetation, the tree produces the mightiest food?

Yet when orthodox nutritionists talk about protein, they stress flesh foods and animal products. They always place animal protein first on their lists. Then they list plant protein, such as beans and grains. If they mention nuts and seeds at all, they put them last.

Even some vegetarians have not given first rank to this most valuable of all concentrated protein. They often stress beans and grains, and list eggs and dairy items above nuts. (A refreshing exception to this lamentable ignorance is the great bodybuilder, Bill Pearl. In his "Wisdom of Pearl" column in the February issue of *Muscle & Fitness*, he listed raw nuts *first* as a meatless protein food.)

A few years ago, I met Franco Columbu when he visited Detroit, Michigan to appear as a guest poser. While I was showing him around town, we discussed diet. When we got to nuts, he became enthusiastic. When I told him I was a vegetarian and ate raw nuts almost daily, he commended me. Franco said when he came to America he was horrified by the way people treated nuts, ruining them by boiling them in oil, roasting them, and adding salt.

Nuts are one of the richest foods. Biologically, they have been classified as a fruit because they contain their own seeds. But because they do not have a meaty, edible peel, nuts are not thought of as a fruit.

The nut is hermetically sealed in its shell to preserve and protect it from contamination. Inside the shell, most nuts are also covered with a skin that is poisonous to bacteria and other microscopic life.

When nuts are ripe, they can be cracked and eaten, or they can be stored for months to be eaten later. Nuts provide everything we can obtain from animal flesh, but in a cleaner, more healthful condition.

Nuts are the best source of protein and fats,

and are rich in vitamins and minerals. These vitamins and minerals are essential in digesting and assimilating protein. Also, most nuts are delicious in their raw state, so they don't have to be cooked.

While the different varieties of nuts vary in their mineral components, their calcium, phosphorus, sulphur, magnesium, manganese, silicon, and chlorine content is high. Although the protein and fat content also are generally high, there is a variance. But don't think that one nut is superior to another because it's higher in protein. Any food item that has more than 5% protein can be considered a protein food. Any food containing more than 10% can be considered a high-protein food. Bodybuilders tend to be overimpressed by protein. Actually a very high (concentrated) protein food may not digest as easily and be assimilated as efficiently as a lower protein food.

Health authority and nutritionist Herbert Shelton writes this about nuts in *Superior Nutrition:* "Rich in protein of high biological value, packed with minerals and vitamins and savoured by nature so that they appeal to the gustatory sense of man, such nuts as the pecan, walnut, almond, Brazil nut . . . are valuable additions to our diet. They are not substitutes for flesh foods—flesh food is the substitute."

Following is a brief nutritional analysis of the most common nuts in America:

Almond

The skin, which is bitter due to its tannic acid content, should be removed. If it isn't, the nut will not taste good, nor digest well. The removal is simple. Just toss the almonds into boiling water. Take the pot off the stove and let the nuts sit in the hot water for two minutes. Then pour off the water and pop the nuts out of their skins.

Analysis (figures indicate percentages): water, 6.0; protein, 24.0; fat, 54.33; carbohydrate, 10.0; fiber, 3.0; mineral salts, 3.0.

Brazil Nut

This uniquely shaped nut is high in fat, protein, calcium, and magnesium.

Analysis: water, 4.8; protein, 17.2; fat, 66.0; carbohydrate (mostly sugar), 5.7; fiber, 3.0; mineral salts, 3.3.

Cashew

This delicious morsel is the fruit of a tropical American tree. The cashew contains a strong acid that is removed by applying low heat. Therefore "raw" cashews are not really raw. The cashew is similar to most other nuts in protein, fat, and carbohydrate content.

Chestnut

Although this is technically a nut, it is unlike any other. It is lower in protein than other nuts, very low in fat, and extremely high in carbohydrate (mostly starch). Because it has to be cooked to be palatable, it could be thought of as a substitute for the potato.

Analysis: water, 6.0; fat, 8.0; protein, 10.0; carbohydrate, 70.0; fiber, 3.0; mineral salts, 2.4.

Coconut

This is the giant of nuts. It is delicious in its natural state, but unfortunately this wholesome food is processed by candy makers and bakers. It should be eaten like most other nuts—whole, raw, and fresh.

Analysis: water, 3.5; protein, 6.5; fat, 57.4; carbohydrate and fiber, 31.5; mineral salts, 1.3.

Hickory Nut

This is a native American nut. Unfortunately, the European settlers of America, ignorant of nutrition, cut down most of the hickory trees for fuel and lumber. The shell of the hickory nut is thick and hard, making it very difficult to crack. However, there is a thin-shelled variety called "Hale's Paper Shell." This rich, tasty nut is unavailable to most Americans.

Analysis: water, 3.7; protein, 15.15; fat, 68.0; carbohydrate (mostly sugar), 12.0; mineral salts, 1.5.

Pistachio

Unfortunately, this delicious nut is difficult to find raw. Most stores carry it roasted and salted, with the shell dyed red! Because it is imported from the Middle East, it's expensive.

Analysis: water, 4.2; protein, 22.5; fat, 54.5; carbohydrate (mostly sugar), 16.0; mineral salts, 3.0. Unlike other nuts, the pistachio contains no fiber.

Walnut

America has its own variety, the black walnut. But most of the walnuts now grown in America are the English variety. The black walnut is the most delicious, but comes in a very hard shell. America has another native walnut, the Butternut, but it is rare.

Analysis:	Black	English	Butternut
Water	2.5	2.5	4.5
Protein	27.5	18.5	27.9
Fats	56.3	64.5	61.2
Carbohydrate	11.7	12.5	3.4
Fiber	1.7	1.4	0.0
Mineral Salts	1.9	1.7	3.0

Pecan

This is the most popular and perhaps most delicious of American nuts. The American Indians stored enormous amounts of them for the winter and spring.

Analysis: water, 3.5; protein, 13.0; fat, 70.8; carbohydrate (mostly sugar), 8.5; fiber, 3.7; mineral salts, 1.5.

Filbert

The filbert is one of the most edible of nuts. The shell is round, easy to crack, and the nut comes out in one piece. The nut is loose inside the shell. Like the pecan, the nut is delicious, with a slight sweet taste. Also called the Hazelnut, it is best eaten right out of the shell. Filberts, as well as pecans and walnuts, are easy to find in the supermarket. The filbert is a popular nut throughout Europe.

Peanut

The peanut is not a nut. It is a legume (a pea or bean) that comes in a hard, dry pod. Like beans, the peanut is high in starch as well as protein. It is fairly high in fat, but not as high as nuts. The peanut contains about 35% protein, which makes it the highest protein food known to man.

Peanuts are usually roasted and are delicious eaten that way, but learn to eat them raw. Always buy them in the shell, unless they are refrigerated in plastic bags. The raw peanut is not as tasty as the roasted one, but most people who eat peanuts raw become accustomed to the taste and like it. Eating them raw will prevent you from overating. Also, there will be much less stomach gas.

Sunflower Seed

Because these seeds are so popular and are so similar to nuts in their composition, they are usually categorized with nuts. Again, these should never be eaten roasted. They are delicious in the raw state. They contain 25% protein, and are high in oil content. Sunflower seeds are popular in Europe, particularly in Eastern Europe. In the Soviet Union they are cultivated as a major food crop. Like nuts, they are rich in minerals and vitamins. They are believed to be good for the eyes.

If you consider only the edible portion, nuts cost more per pound than meat. But—and this is a very important *but*—a quarter pound of nuts or seeds is worth at least a pound of meat. That's mainly because:

- Meat is almost always eaten cooked, which destroys much of its food value;
- Meat takes a long time to digest and leaves much acid waste; and
- Meat is mineral-poor, which makes it difficult to digest and assimilate.

From this discussion, I hope you'll begin to see that nuts are not only the best form of protein, but, as an all-round food, they're vastly superior to meat and animal products. There is no reason to substitute meat, cheese, and eggs for nuts and seeds.

For health, muscle, and strength, explore the world of nuts. Remember: *meat is the substitute.*

Get Supercharged by Carbohydrate Loading

by Armand Tanny

A nutritional technique of endurance athletes, *carbohydrate loading*, may offer increased muscularity and extra energy for bodybuilders in intense training. But the staple food of the program, pasta, may become passé if the more promising liquid supplements continue to outperform spaghetti.

The popular carbohydrate loading regimen stems from 1967 research which demonstrated that a particular eating and training pattern could produce great endurance. That pattern involved athletes first depleting their glycogen (body fuel) stores through an intense workout. Next, they followed a low-carbohydrate diet for three days. Then, as a final step, they went on a high-carbohydrate diet for three days. The end result was a high glycogen fuel supply and heightened endurance.

The capacity to store glycogen determines the amount of endurance. The more you can store, the longer and harder you can go before you "hit the wall." In the jargon of endurance athletics, "hitting the wall" means reaching that point in an event when a spirited performance suddenly becomes a painful ordeal. This usually occurs after 1.5–2 hours of continuous strenuous exercise when the body has run out of glycogen, its high-octane fuel. Breathing becomes labored, legs become leaden, and the athlete slows to a snail's pace.

WHAT IS GLYCOGEN?

Glycogen is the stored high-octane fuel of the body, and the glycogen stored in muscles is the main fuel for heavy workouts.

Glycogen comes from the carbohydrates we eat. The body converts carbohydrates to glucose, which the liver releases into the bloodstream to fuel physical processes. Any excess is converted into glycogen, which is how the body stores carbohydrates. Glycogen can be changed back into glucose when the glucose level in the bloodstream falls.

The liver is the main organ for synthesizing glycogen from glucose. Skeletal, cardiac, and smooth muscle tissue store some glycogen, as do practically all organs (in small amounts).

Muscle uses equal amounts of fat and carbohydrate during moderate exercise. But for

immediate supply of natural sugar energy.

If you eat them with nuts or cereals, the digestion is slowed. As a result, you don't get that surge of energy. If you want to make a meal out of dried fruits, add some bananas or apples instead of nuts or cereals.

There are many kinds of dried fruit. These include dried pineapple, papaya, cherries, and nectarines, as well as the more common ones such as dried apricots, pears, and apples.

Before we discuss the more common dried fruits, remember these rules:

- Do not buy sulphured fruits, and
- Don't buy sugared fruits.

Unfortunately, most dried fruit you find in supermarkets has been treated with sulphur dioxide. This is done to make the fruit look lighter and prettier, and to retain some of the moisture.

Like all chemical preservatives, the sulphur on the fruits acts as a poison to your system. The sulphurous acid used to treat dried fruits seriously harms the kidneys, which have to remove all added sulphur from the body. The sulphur also retards the formation of red blood corpuscles and destroys the vitamins in the fruit. So avoid sulphured dried fruits.

Unless you have access to a health-food store, you may find that raisins are the only dried, unsulphured fruit you can buy. Be sure you get the regular dark-colored raisins. The so-called "golden" yellow raisins are that color because of the added sulphur dioxide.

Now let's look at three of the most easily obtainable dried fruits, and see what they can do for you.

Figs

Did you know that the ancient Roman wrestlers trained on an exclusive diet of figs? Actually, dried figs are one of the best bodybuilding foods you can find.

Chemical analysis shows a remarkable similarity between the composition of figs and human milk. Mother's milk can double the size of an infant in 180 days. No wonder the Romans thought so highly of figs!

Figs have the added advantage of being slightly laxative (as are all dried fruits). They supply needed fiber, along with mineral salts.

You'll probably find two varieties of dried figs: the black (called Black Mission) and the brown (usually a Calimyrna type). Both are excellent. The black variety generally is higher in calcium, while the brown is usually a little sweeter.

I find that slicing or blending soaked figs into unsweetened apple sauce makes an outstanding super-energy dish.

Dates

I'll bet you didn't know that dates are a complete protein. They have all eight essential amino acids, and while their protein content is only 2.2%, the protein is easily assimilated.

Dates are said to be such a complete food that desert tribes in Africa and Asia often live for months at a time on nothing more than dates and milk, or dates and oranges.

Dates are 70% sugar—and that's *natural* sugar that your body can immediately use with no ill effects.

If you shop around, you can find more than half a dozen different varieties of dates. Some are sweeter, others are more moist. Probably the king of all the varieties is the Medajool. It's twice the size of the other dates and has a rich, creamy texture. The most common variety is the Degleet Noor, which has a sweet, buttery taste.

And don't forget date sugar, which is made entirely from powdered dates. It looks like very coarse, extra-dark brown sugar. If you need a natural sweetener, date sugar is best. It supplies far more nutrients than honey, maple syrup, or other sugar substitutes. Get some for sprinkling over fruit salads.

Raisins

This is the most common dried fruit, and it's very good. Raisins are 2.6% protein, 3.3% fat, and 76% sugar. They're very rich in iron and are a great blood builder.

Here's a good way to make two energy drinks from the same quantity of raisins. Soak a cup of raisins overnight in a quart of distilled water. In the morning, pour the water from the soaked raisins into another jar. This gives you a quart of very sweet, mineral-enriched water to drink.

Now take the soaked raisins and put them into a quart of apple juice. Blend the raisins and apple juice. This makes a great drink by itself, or you can use it as a base for a high-protein or energy drink.

There are many other dried fruits you may want to try. If you ever find some *unsugared* dried pineapple, I guarantee you'll make it one of your high-energy favorites!

Just remember: high-energy workouts demand high-energy foods, not empty calories. For your sugar needs, reach for the dried fruits—and you'll never feel that mid-workout energy crash.

Vegetables for Bodybuilding

by Bill Dobbins

If you ask the average bodybuilder what kind of diet he thinks will help him to produce a championship physique, he'll probably tell you, "Lots of protein, very little carbohydrate." What he really means is a lot of meat, fish, and fowl and very few vegetables. Modern nutritionists would tend to frown upon this theory.

There's a big difference between a training diet and precontest diet. A precontest diet tends to be unbalanced and relatively unhealthy. What a bodybuilder needs for really intense training during the rest of the year is a diet that provides him with all the nutrients, vitamins, and minerals his body requires. These things are better derived from food than from supplements. Supplements should be just that—a *supplement,* not the mainstay of your nutritional intake.

Meat, fish, and fowl contain a great deal of complete protein, but they also contain a relatively large number of calories and, in many cases, a great deal of fat. However, vegetables can also be a good source of protein, even for the competitive bodybuilder—as the ageless Bill Pearl, a vegetarian, has proven. And vegetables can supply vitamins and minerals that are lacking in meat and fish.

Vegetables, unfortunately, are fragile. Improper handling and cooking can ruin both their nutritional value and taste. Therefore, in order to make the most of vegetables in your training diet, some attention must be paid to buying, preparing and serving them.

SALADS

The best way to prepare many vegetables is to do as little as possible to them. Many can be served raw in salads. A lot of people believe that salads should consist mostly of lettuce and tomatoes, with maybe some cucumbers or mushrooms added. But salads can come in an almost endless variety, providing everything from protein to fiber, and they can be a taste treat as well.

You can serve salads before the main meal, or make an entire meal out of them. If you choose your vegetables properly, you can eat a great deal and yet ingest relatively few calories. This is an advantage when you want to stay cut up, but are getting tired of never feeling full after a meal. A simple table of caloric values will let you know which vegetables are low in calories (like the mushrooms and cucumbers mentioned above) and which are high (avocados, for example).

Food should be pleasing to the eye as well as the taste buds, and you can easily create a variety of attractive-looking meals with very little effort. Remember, however, if you cover your salads with vinegar and oil, that oil is adding around 100 calories a tablespoon to what you are eating. True, you are keeping the carbohydrate down, but you might consider using a diet dressing instead, or simply adding lemon juice to your salads.

Here is a sample of the kind of salad you can make into a main course:

Vegetable Salad

Lettuce
Spinach
Tomatoes
Cucumbers
Artichoke hearts
Broccoli
Mushrooms
Asparagus tips
Carrots (shredded)
Shrimp, tuna or protein powder
    (optional)

On a large platter, place bed of lettuce (or spinach, or both). Around the edge of the platter, place the tops of raw broccoli stalks, asparagus tips (canned), tomatoes cut into quarters and other vegetables in any attractive pattern. Add shrimp or tuna if desired, or sprinkle salad with protein powder.

KEEP VEGETABLES COOL AND DRY

Whether you plan to use your vegetables raw in a salad or to cook them, they should be kept cool and dry in the meantime. If they are washed, they should be dried off immediately and returned to the refrigerator. They should also be kept out of the light. Left at room temperature and in the light for only a few hours, most fresh vegetables will lose a great deal of folic acid, Vitamin B-2, and 50% or more of their Vitamin C content.

Studies have shown that when whole vegetables are boiled (or soaked) for only four minutes, 20%–45% of their mineral content and 75% of their sugar passes into the water. Vitamins C, D, and the many B vitamins pass out of the vegetables and dissolve in water as quickly as sugar dissolves in coffee. Since vegetables are frequently soaked before and after cooking for even longer periods, as much as 75%–100% of the sugars, minerals and water-soluble vitamins are often lost.

DO NOT PEEL VEGETABLES

When you peel vegetables like potatoes, parsnips, or eggplant, you're throwing away nutrients for no reason. Don't peel vegetables unless the skin is tough, bitter, or too uneven to be thoroughly cleaned. Remember, the average family annually throws away potato parings equivalent in protein to 60 steaks, equivalent in Vitamin C to 95 glasses of orange juice, and equivalent in iron to 500 eggs.

DO ANYTHING BUT BOIL

When you boil vegetables you end up with highly nutritive water, but fairly useless vegetables. Instead, you should bake, broil, or even steam vegetables. The first two methods involve no water at all, and the last only involves minimal contact with water. If you have any water left after steaming (and you should only use a little in the first place), serve it with the vegetables. It's full of good stuff.

Except for vegetables that are especially tough and fibrous, like artichokes, keep cooking to a minimum. Pressure cookers are good for vegetables because they get the job done fast and don't let any of the steam escape.

Also, don't salt vegetables before cooking. Salt attracts moisture, so when a vegetable is salted prior to cooking, its juices (which carry vitamins, minerals, and sugars, as well as flavor) are drawn out. Salted spinach, for instance, loses 47% of its iron content during cooking. However, it only loses 19% if unsalted. Of course, used raw in a salad, it loses none.

SUMMING UP

- Your vegetables should be as fresh as possible.
- Avoid prolonged contact between vegetables and water while washing, preparing or cooking.
- Keep vegetables chilled and out of the light.
- Broil, bake, or steam, but do not boil vegetables.
- Cook vegetables in the shortest time possible and avoid overcooking.

- Frying vegetables in oil supplies vitamins B-6, E, K, and essential fatty acids, but adds a lot of extra calories. Also, if heat is too high, some of the B vitamins can be destroyed.
- Do not peel or salt vegetables prior to cooking.

JUICING

A convenient way to prepare vegetables is by running them through a juicer and reducing them to liquid. Today, there are numerous machines that can turn carrots into carrot juice in the blink of an eye. But there are a number of possible drawbacks to consuming vegetables in this form.

First of all, there are those who claim that whenever you alter the form of vegetables or fruits you lose some of the nutritional value. This view holds that apples are better for you than apple sauce or apple juice. Additionally, when you drink vegetable or fruit juices, the food bypasses the saliva in the mouth which is supposed to play an important role in the digestive process. This may overtax the body's gastric-juice supply.

Also, when you turn vegetables into juice, you tend to increase your caloric intake. A whole, raw carrot contains approximately 80 calories. But it takes a lot of carrots to make a glass of carrot juice. Therefore, your vegetable snack in juice form might be giving you 300 or 400 calories you don't need.

However, if you do decide to make yourself some vegetable juice (and, in moderation, there's no reason why not), don't make the mistake that a lot of health-food freaks do. Be sure what you make is palatable. If you throw a mishmash of incompatible vegetables into a juicer, you are liable to come out with something that tastes like grass, or worse. So use some restraint and common sense in your experiments.

VEGETABLES FOREVER

In order to get the most out of vegetables, take the trouble to sit down with a food chart and see exactly what the different vegetables contain. Potatoes, for example, are low in calories and high in protein. Mustard greens contain a lot of calcium. Carrots provide a tremendous source of Vitamin A. Each vegetable has something special to offer. Get to know them and they can do you a lot of good.

TRAINING PROGRAMS

How the Mr. Olympia Winners Trained

by Bill Reynolds

Five men have won the Mr. Olympia title since Joe Weider inaugurated the competition in 1965. Here I have selected a different body part routine from each of these champions. Together, these routines make up almost a complete body workout. The only body parts left out are the calves and abdominals.

All of these routines have been published in past issues of *Muscle & Fitness* and other Joe Weider bodybuilding magazines. But I think they are well worth reprinting for all those readers who may have missed the workouts the first time they appeared in print.

ARMS—LARRY SCOTT

Larry Scott, winner of the '65 and '66 Mr. Olympia contests, the first two ever staged, was renowned for his superb upper arm development. Larry, who was approximately 5'8" and weighed 210 pounds in contest shape, displayed massive, and well-shaped 20.5-inch upper arms. He trained his biceps and triceps three days per week after completing his deltoid

routine. Here was a typical Larry Scott upper arm routine:

1. Dumbbell Preacher Curl: 80-lb. dumbbells, 4 × 6 plus 4–6 burns (four sets of six repetitions, plus 4–6 burns, or short half curls from the starting point of the movement).
2. Barbell Preacher Curl: 130–140 lbs., 4 × 6–8 plus 3–4 burns.
3. Standing Reverse Curl: 120–130 lbs., 4 × 6.
4. Spider Bench Curl: 100–110 lbs., 4 × 6.
5. Lying Triceps Extension (EZ-curl bar): 200+ lbs., 4 × 6 plus 4–6 burns, supersetted with
6. Pulley Pushdown: 100–120 lbs., 4 × 6 plus 4–5 burns.
7. Triceps Kickback: 60–70 lbs., 4 × 8.

THIGHS—SERGIO OLIVA

Oliva dominated the Mr. Olympia competition from 1967 through 1969. Many bodybuilding fans still consider him to be the best bodybuilder of all time. Sergio's thighs in particular were phenomenally developed. The following was a typical Oliva thigh routine:

1. Squats: 8–10 sets, working up from a light weight to a maximum double or single rep with 500–600 lbs.
2. Leg Extensions: 5–6 × 10–15.
3. Leg Curls: 8–10 × 10–15.
4. Lunges: 3–5 × 10–15 (precontest training phase only).

SHOULDERS—ARNOLD SCHWARZENEGGER

With seven Mr. Olympia wins (1970–75, and 1980) to his credit, Arnold is the best-known competitor in bodybuilding history. His combination of huge mass, flawless proportions, great genetic muscle shape, classic symmetry, and incredible onstage charisma has never been equaled. Here's one of the Austrian Oak's deltoid workouts:

1. Rotating Dumbbell Presses: 4 × 8–10.
2. Seated Press Behind Neck: 4 × 8–10.
3. Seated Bent Laterals: 4 × 8–10.
4. Low Incline Lying Side Laterals: 4 × 10.
5. Alternate Front Dumbbell Raises: 4 × 8–10.
6. Cable Side Laterals: 4 × 8–10.

Larry Scott blasts his arms with Preacher Curls.

Sergio Oliva, one of the legends of bodybuilding.

The Austrian Oak, Arnold Schwarzenegger.

BACK—FRANCO COLUMBU

Columbu won the Mr. Olympia title twice (1976, 1981), and was runner-up to Arnold Schwarzenegger several times. He recovered from a serious knee injury in order to regain the 1981 title. Franco's back was always phenomenal. Here is a typical Columbu lat workout:

1. Wide Grip Chins: 6 × 10–15 (with added weight).
2. T-Bar Rowing: 4 × 10.
3. Seated Pulley Rowing: 4 × 10.
4. One-Arm Dumbbell Rowing: 3 × 10, supersetted with . . .
5. Close-Grip Chins: 3 × 10.

CHEST—FRANK ZANE

Like Oliva, Frank Zane won three consecutive Mr. Olympia titles (1977–79). When he puts his hands on his hips, pulls his elbows forward, and flexes his pectorals, Frank's chest muscles appear slashed to ribbons. Here's one of his chest workouts.

1. Bench Press: 5 × 12–6 (increasing the weight and decreasing the reps with each successive set).
2. Incline Dumbbell Press: 3 × 15–6 (increasing weight and decreasing reps as in the Bench Press).
3. Flyes (on a slight incline): 3 × 10.
4. Cross-Bench Dumbbell Pullover: 3 × 10.

Franco Columbu doing Seated Pulley Rowing.

SUMMARY

Of course, all of these superstars have used the Weider Training Principles in their workouts. Most frequently used have been the Weider Muscle Priority Training Principle, the Weider Overload Training Principle, and the Weider Quality Training Principle.

Any reader can adapt these Mr. Olympia training routines to his or her own training level. If you're a beginner, use the same exercises but do no more than 5–6 total sets. Intermediates should not exceed 10 total sets and advanced bodybuilders should do no more than 15 sets per body part. By following these guidelines you should make excellent progress on any of these five Olympian routines!

Frank Zane pyramids Bench Presses for maximum effect.

Tim Belknap's Training Routine

by Mike Mentzer

If Tim Belknap had been born in ancient Sparta, he would have been taken into the mountains as a child and abandoned. As it was, Tim grew up in modern-day Rockville, Ill., where he was so puny as a result of diabetes that his high school classmates—including girls—used to beat him up.

When he could stand it no longer, Tim joined a health club. That was in March 1977. Tim made spectacular gains, building one of the brawniest physiques of all time. He won a series of bodybuilding contests and now is a contender for the 1981 Mr. America title.

It was while training at the health club in Rockville that Tim made a discovery that was to profoundly alter the course of his life.

"I'll never forget it," he told me. "Somebody brought in a copy of *Muscle Builder* (now *Muscle & Fitness*). I was amazed at the before-and-after photos of the top champions. If they could transform their bodies so dramatically, I told myself, so could I.

"*Muscle Builder* became my bible. It was in the pages of that magazine that I learned how to eat properly to gain muscle. I increased my calorie intake dramatically and ate a more balanced diet."

Tim now had a direction, a sense of purpose that started him on an exciting journey. No longer content with a conditioning program, he searched through the pages of *Muscle Builder* for a more advanced routine. His first discovery was the Weider Split System. Anxious to increase his mass, he continued on a high-calorie diet and started on a split routine, training his legs, back, and biceps on Mondays and Thursdays, and his chest, delts, and triceps on Tuesdays and Fridays. He performed the basic exercises, usually three per body part, doing five sets of each exercise.

For a short while Tim made nice gains on his new program. But soon his prodigious capacity to build muscle fast required an even more advanced routine.

"I began to read the articles that Joe Weider and you, Mike, were writing on the importance of intensity in training," he said. "I lowered my sets and began training much heavier. I knew I couldn't look like Zane. I'm not just saying this to flatter you, but I began comparing my physique to yours and Casey Viator's. Because I wanted to be thick and heavily muscled, I trained like Joe and you advocated in your articles—intense and heavy."

Tim's new approach worked like a dream. He continued to add to his already burgeoning mass. By 1979, at the age of 20 and with only two years of solid training under his belt, 5'5" Tim weighed 220 pounds! He was squatting with 655 pounds for 20 reps, bench pressing 485 pounds for 10 reps, and curling a 225-pound barbell for 10 reps.

Encouraged by his incredible rate of progress, Tim thought it was time to compete. To get his feet wet, he entered the Jr. Mr. Mid-America in May 1979 and was disappointed with his sixth-place finish. Hoping to redeem himself, he entered the Region 6 contest in November of 1979. This time he didn't even place.

"The reason I did so poorly was that my symmetry was so bad," he said. "My pecs were underdeveloped, my shoulders were narrow, my abs were smooth, and my legs were way too big for the rest of my body. I also needed more separation everywhere. I decided to take a year off from competing and work on my weak points."

Tim's remedial program began with a dietary analysis. Much to his surprise, he learned that he was consuming an average of 6,600 calories a day. No wonder he lacked separation! Immediately he cut back to 2,500–3,000 calories a

day, with a minimum of 200 grams of carbohydrate. By reducing his calories and keeping his carbohydrates at a high level, he could reduce his body fat levels, yet allow himself enough energy to train with sufficient intensity. Before he knew it, he was getting more dense and cut.

Unlike many bodybuilders with weak points, Tim didn't concentrate on them. He knew intuitively that it was better to work the entire body more intensely and that eventually, as his physique matured, the weak parts would come up to equality.

Intent on perfecting his physique, he resolved to make each training session harder than the last one. Tim's tenacity was almost palpable. He later described his training at the time, "I learned never to go easy on myself. In the gym I would see people talking between sets and then doing a few reps, feel a little discomfort and stop. Not me. I wasn't going to let anything stand in my way. Every set I did was to failure. Every time I went to the gym I tried to make the training hurt more. If it didn't, I'd train even more intensely next time."

Besides training more intensely, Tim stopped

powerlifting, since he felt it was making him appear too blocky. Once he realized that his penchant for performing single attempts with very heavy weights was an ego thing and a hindrance to his bodybuilding progress, he dropped the practice. Instead, he fashioned a routine that revolved around bodybuilding exercises aimed at shaping and reproportioning his physique.

Tim now trained six days a week, hitting each body part just twice a week in order not to overtrain. Below is his routine:

Monday and Thursday

Legs:
1. Hack Squat Variation 4 × 15 (done for sweep of the outer thigh)
2. Leg Extensions 4 × 15–25
3. Leg Curls 5 × 15
4. Toe Raises and Donkey Raises supersetted for a total of 10 sets (15–20 reps per set)

Tuesday and Friday

Chest:
1. Bench Presses 4 × 8–12 (not for development but for fun)
2. Incline Presses 3 × 8–10 (done without warm-up) since the bench presses served as sufficient warm-up)
3. Low Incline Flyes, 3 × 10
4. Dips 1 × 15–25 done merely as a finishing-off exercise

Back:
1. Wide-Grip Chins 2 × 10 (done as a warm-up, no weight)
2. Wide-Grip Pulldowns to chest 3 × 12–15
3. Wide-Grip Seated Cable Rows 3 × 12–15
4. Narrow-Grip Seated Cable Rows 3 × 12–15
5. Pullovers 3 × 10–12
6. Stiff-Leg Deadlifts 3 × 10–12
7. Hyperextensions 3 × 15–25 (no weight)

Wednesday and Saturday

Shoulders:
1. Presses Behind Neck 3 × 8–12
2. Lateral Raises 3 × 8–12
3. Rear Laterals with cables 3 × 8–12 (only done three weeks before a contest since the Press Behind Neck was usually sufficient)

Arms:
1. Close-Grip Bench Presses 3 × 10–12

2. Decline Triceps Extensions 3 × 10–12
3. Pressdowns 3 × 10–12
4. Barbell Curls 3 × 10
5. Seated Dumbbell Curls 3 × 10
6. Cable Curls 3 × 10

Abdominals:
1. Crunch Sit-Ups (5 × 20–30) supersetted with
2. Leg Raises with cable (5 × 20–30)
3. Side Bends 5 × 30–50

Tim started this program in late 1979. By the early part of 1980, he felt he had sufficiently improved his weak points and lack of separation, so he began training and dieting in earnest for the Jr. Mr. Illinois, to be held in April. He gradually reduced his calorie intake to 1,200 a day and intensified his training even more. A couple of weeks before the contest he went to Florida to get some sun. Upon his return he won the contest handily.

Spurred on by his first competitive success, Tim decided to enter the Mr. Illinois in November. Sticking with the same training program, he cut his calorie intake even further—to 1,000 a day. He entered the contest highly defined and separated. But because he continued to consume just the right combination of simple and complex carbohydrates, he maintained his considerable mass. Tim had weighed 215 pounds the year before when he failed to place at the Region 6 contest. While he won the Mr. Illinois weighing only five pounds less at 210, the difference in his appearance was astounding. The fat that Tim lost was almost completely replaced by muscle, which explains the relatively small body weight change.

You might think that with two successive wins to his credit, Tim would be satisfied. Hardly. Feeling that he could be even more cut up than he'd been at the Mr. Illinois, Tim set his sights on the more prestigious Mr. Midwest contest to be held in March of 1981. Satisfied that he was on the right track with his training, he stayed on the same routine he had used for the Mr. Illinois. He adhered to a strict diet all winter, allowing only a few pounds of fat to accumulate. Then with a couple of weeks to go to the contest, he reduced his calories to 900 a day. Such a diet is difficult for anyone to adhere to, but for a guy weighing 220 pounds who hoists tons of iron every day, it was torture.

"Sticking to a 900-calories-a-day diet is really more mental than anything," Tim said. "If you are totally focused on what you want to accomplish, nothing will stand in your way. When I was tempted to go off my diet, all I did was think about the contest. Eventually the temptation went away."

Tim's iron-willed discipline paid off handsomely. The 1981 Mr. Midwest became his third straight victory in less than a year.

Now that he has won everything there is to win in his part of the country, Tim feels that the only contest left to enter on the amateur level is the Mr. America, to be held in Las Vegas, Nev. on Sept. 5. When I asked if he plans to change his routine while preparing for this prestigious contest, Tim said, "The only thing I am going to do differently is start my training and diet earlier than usual and then come to Gold's to train for a couple of months before the contest and have Joe Weider teach me to pose and control my muscles. But I am going to train even harder than before; I'm going to train like an animal, full of rage and fire."

Whew, is this kid psyched! He's really hungry for that Mr. America title. I'd better advise Pete Grymkowski at Gold's to take out fire insurance before Tim arrives.

Chest Training My Way

by Roy Callender, with Bill Reynolds

When I was growing up in the Barbados, I was almost consumed by the desire to build a massive, well-defined physique. Looking back now on this boyhood dream, I think I've reached my goal, particularly when it comes to chest development. It wasn't easy to actualize my boyhood dream, however. I made many mistakes in both my training and diet as I was coming up the bodybuilding ladder, and if I've succeeded as a bodybuilder it's only because I've learned from my mistakes and never repeated them.

For optimal chest development, a beginning and intermediate bodybuilder must do the basic chest exercises—Barbell Bench Presses, Barbell Incline Presses and Parallel Bar Dips—for his pectorals, and he must try to increase the volume of his ribcage at an early stage of training. My basic errors in chest training were: failure to expand my ribcage when I first started bodybuilding, and sticking too long with basic chest movement, particularly the Bench Press.

The ribcage can be expanded much more easily during the teenage years than later in life. Ribcage expansion is accomplished by stretching and gradually lengthening the cartilages

connecting your ribs to your sternum (breast bone). By the time you're in your 20s, these cartilages harden and lose their youthful pliability, so it becomes more difficult to stretch them.

Stretching the rib cartilage and thus expanding the ribcage is accomplished by supersetting Breathing Squats with either Straight-Arm Barbell Pullovers, Bent-Arm Barbell Pullovers, or Cross-Bench Dumbbell Pullovers. I prefer the Straight-Arm Pullovers, because Cross-Bench Pullovers seem to involve my latissimus dorsi muscles excessively. In fact, when done with the head hanging off the end of a bench, Bent-Arm Pullovers are more of a lat exercise than a chest exercise.

To perform Straight-Arm Pullovers correctly, begin by lying back lengthwise along a flat exercise bench. Be sure your body is positioned so your head rests *on* the bench. Place your feet firmly on the floor on each side of the bench to balance your body.

Next, grasp a light barbell. At the start of the movement your arms should be straight and the barbell should be supported at arms' length directly above your chest.

69

Pulley Crossovers: "This exercise is everyone's precontest favorite for etching striations across the pecs."

From this starting position, slowly lower the barbell backward in a semicircle to a position as far behind and below your head as possible. Keep your arms straight throughout the movement. As you lower the weight, take in the deepest possible breath, timing the oxygen intake so your lungs reach full capacity as the barbell reaches the low point of the movement. Then hold your breath and return the barbell to the starting point before exhaling.

Breathing Squats are merely high-rep-low-weight Full Squats in which a deep-breathing pattern is used. You should breathe in and out fully several times before each rep. Hold the final breath while you squat down, then exhale at about the halfway point as you come back up.

I recommend sets of 25 reps in your Breathing Squats, utilizing the following numbers of breaths between each rep:

Rep Numbers	Number of Breaths
1–10	3
11–20	4
21–25	5

Beginning bodybuilders should do one superset of 25 Breathing Squats and 25 Straight-Arm Pullovers, in which you also use deep breathing (in a superset, of course, you take no rest between exercises). After six weeks of training, you can progress to doing two supersets, with a rest interval of 3–4 minutes between supersets. Following an additional six weeks of consistent training you can progress to doing three of these supersets. I don't believe you'll ever need to do more than three such Breathing Squat/Straight-Arm Pullover supersets.

If you're still a teenager, you can expect to expand your ribcage almost every month that you use this recommended routine. The result will be a broad, deep ribcage, that will support a perfectly balanced chest.

Once you're past the age of 20, your ribcage expansion will be slower, but you will—with diligence—be able to achieve the same ultimate results. It's just that it'll take you 2–3 times as long, and it will take 2–3 times as much effort. I know this from experience, because I made the mistake of waiting until my mid-20s to start working my ribcage.

As mentioned earlier, my second mistake was sticking to basic chest exercises, particularly the Bench Press, for too long. In the early days, the essence of bodybuilding to me was to pack on all the muscle mass I could. And, of course, basic

exercises are good for building mass. My chest muscles grew rapidly from Bench Presses. Soon I was doing 20–30 sets of Bench Presses in each chest workout.

Unfortunately, I got so carried away by my bench pressing that I neglected my upper chest development. Sure, I did a few sets of Incline Presses in each workout, but it was hardly enough to compensate for all the bench pressing I was doing and its effect on my lower pectorals.

Flat Bench Flyes: "A fine movement for most bodybuilders because it gives you both pec mass and shape."

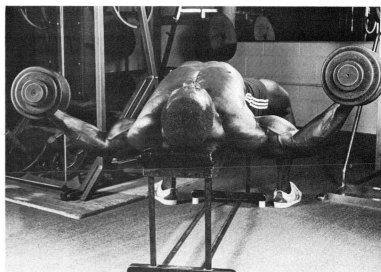

Even though I won the IFBB Mr. World title before going into pro wrestling in 1970, my pecs were badly out of balance. The lower part of my pectorals was so huge in comparison to the upper that my chest muscles looked "droopy."

When I made my bodybuilding comeback in 1977, I decided right off to correct this imbalance in my chest development. I found the solution to my problem in the Weider Muscle Priority Training Principle. It was immediately clear to me that I should shift the bulk of my attention in my chest workouts to my upper pectorals. In time, this would give me the balanced development I wanted.

I started doing a lot of Presses and Flyes on an incline bench. Ultimately, I found that exercises done on a 45-degree incline bench stressed my frontal deltoids a bit too much. If you're after upper pectoral development, I recommend using a 30-degree incline bench. Presses and Flyes done on a 30-degree incline bench stress the upper pectorals directly and with a minimum of deltoid and triceps involvement.

After a few weeks of concentrating on Incline Presses, I completely dropped the barbell variation in favor of dumbbells. Range of motion is the problem with Barbell Incline Presses. I can get a much greater range of motion by using dumbbells.

I do very long workouts. My chest workout lasts 1.5–2 hours. I begin by doing 15–20 sets of Dumbbell Incline Presses, followed by about 10 sets of Incline Flyes. These two movements, which thoroughly bomb my upper pectorals, have enabled me to achieve balanced chest development at last.

The rest of my chest routine consists of 6–10 sets each of Wide-Grip Parallel Bar Dips (or Dips done with a regular grip while leaning my torso forward), Straight-Arm Pullovers (or occasionally Bent-Arm Pullovers, Flat-Bench Flyes, or Pec-Deck Flyes for a little extra variety) and Cable Crossovers. I do the Crossovers in a variety of positions to bomb my pecs, particularly the inner edges, from all angles.

I train my chest every third day. I don't use a specific number of sets for each movement in my chest workout. Instead, I go strictly by feel (the Weider Instinctive Training Principle). My body tells me when it's had enough of each exercise; then I go on to the next one. My end objective in each workout is to get a fully fatigued, tightly pumped feeling in my pectorals.

My chest routine will be far too taxing for beginning and intermediate bodybuilders, as

Pec Deck Flyes: "When I feel some need for variety in my chest routine, I include a few sets of these."

Precontest Training
1. Dumbbell Incline Presses: 4–6 × 8–12, supersetted with . . .
2. Incline Flyes: 4–6 × 10–12
3. Parallel Bar Dips: 3–5 × 10–12, supersetted with . . .
4. Straight-Arm Pullovers: 3–5 × 15–20
5. Flat-Bench Flyes: 3–5 × 10-12, supersetted with . . .
6. Cable Crossovers: 3–5 × 10–15

People at contests compliment me on my chest development, but I'm far from satisfied with it. There's a lot more I can do with my chest—a *lot more*. Olympian though it may already be, it can be made even better!

Parallel Bar Dips: "When I have access to the appropriate equipment, I like to do my Dips with a very wide grip."

well as for many advanced men and women. Most individuals would quickly overtrain if they did my routine regularly. So I would like to offer four alternative chest workouts geared to bodybuilders with varied amounts of training experience. You can use any of these routines two or three days a week (Mondays-Thursdays, or Mondays-Wednesdays-Fridays):

Beginning Level
1. Barbell Bench Presses: 3–4 × 6–10
2. Dumbbell Incline Presses: 3 × 6–10

Intermediate Level
1. Barbell Bench Presses: 4–5 × 6–10
2. Dumbbell Incline Presses: 3–4 × 6–10
3. Flat-Bench Flyes: 3–4 × 8–12

Advanced Level/Off-Season Contest Level Training
1. Dumbbell Incline Presses: 4–6 × 6–10
2. Incline Flyes: 3–4 × 8–12
3. Parallel Bar Dips: 3–4 × 8–12
4. Pec Deck Flyes: 3–4 × 8–12
5. Cable Crossovers: 1–2 × 10–15

Incline Dumbbell Press: "I prefer to use dumbbells, rather than a barbell, in the Incline Press because they give me a greater range of motion."

Incline Flyes: "By filling in my upper pectorals, this movement has done much to balance my chest development."

Lat Machine Pulldown: "Chins and Pulldowns are the basic lat width movements (start, above left). Be sure to pull your elbows down and back (midpoint, above right). You can do Pulldowns to the front or back of your neck."

set of lat work. Grab a stationary bar with one hand and stretch, or hang with both hands from a chinning bar. Hang from the bar with a wide grip and swing from side to side to stretch the serratus and lower lats. The action keeps the blood in the area, makes you more flexible, and helps develop the lower lats. Although stretching is important for all muscles. I have stretched more for the back and the lats than for any other areas.

Another good way to bring out back muscularity is posing—e.g., doing the double biceps pose and holding it for a long time, bringing the shoulders back, turning the head to one side, and lifting the ribcage up to bring out the cuts in the area of the lower trapezius, the outer part of the lats, and the part where the spinal erectors tie into the trapezius.

Joe Weider has helped me a lot by pointing out the little posing secrets that bring out my muscularity. If you don't do these things while posing in shows, it's assumed that you don't have a certain type of development.

Many bodybuilders are able to build a big back in a short period but don't have full control

of the back muscles. They simply haven't practiced their posing. The back is the most detailed area of the whole body. Backs on top physique men like Roy Callender, Albert Beckles, and Franco Columbu—all with thick spinal erectors and lats—are sensational. But too many guys never reach their full potential because of their meager back development.

During my training period for the 1979 Olympia, I suffered a blow to my lower back while filming a TV show. The area became swollen and tender, and I had to baby it in my workouts. When I started working it fully, it didn't respond properly. Two weeks before the contest, the mirror indicated my back was not up to par. I have seen the same thing happen before with other body parts.

One main difficulty of bodybuilding competition is to get every body part to peak together. Normally good areas sometimes get neglected, and lose size. With the contest nearing, I began to work my back several days in a row. By show time it was up to par. I've had to bring up my quadriceps in much the same way just before show time with numerous daily sets of Leg Extensions. These emergency procedures have always worked well for me.

When the back becomes finely developed, the intercostals tie into the obliques, and the obliques tie into the spinal erectors. With thick, detailed development and low body fat, you stand a better chance in any contest. My back has always been a good area, but I know I can make it still better. I've had bad luck in the past with different back injuries due to carelessness, but I've always been able to recover.

A bodybuilder has to know how to deal with injuries. He knows their causes and what it takes to make them better. That's one good reason for having many back exercises you can do. If you have a minor back spasm, you refrain from Top Deadlifts and One-Arm Rows and resort to Pulldowns, which help stretch the afflicted area and relieve the tension. With experience you learn to clear the hurdles.

My back responded well right from the beginning of my bodybuilding career, but it didn't get real good until 1976 when I started doing a lot of Bent-Over Barbell Rows.

Seated Pulley Rowing: "I like this variation of Rowing because it builds both width and thickness into the lats."

Pulldowns and Chins will develop wide, high lats, but rowing develops overall back thickness. I prefer the One-Arm Dumbbell Rows now because I can brace myself better, thus preventing lower back strain.

My present back program is the result of more than 20 years of experience. Though I wish I knew then what I know now, I still find bodybuilding a learning experience. Bit by bit my back improves. I think anyone needs the best back he or she can get to qualify for the most respected title of all: Bodybuilder.

One-Arm Pulley Rowing: "This is one exercise in which the stretch at the start is vital. Notice the exaggerated range of motion I can achieve."

Barbell Shrugs: "Done with either a barbell or two dumbbells. Shrugs fill in my trapezius muscles."

High Pulley Rowing: "Variety is the spice of life in back training. That's why I like to vary the angles of movements like this."

Terrific Thighs

by Lou Ferrigno, as told to Bill Reynolds

· By the age of 18 I had been bodybuilding for a year or so, and my upper body had become fairly massive. But my leg development, particularly my thighs, had not kept pace. I had made the classic beginner's mistake of training to build a showy upper body while neglecting my leg development.

I realized that if I was to succeed as a bodybuilder, I would need to bring my legs into proportion with my upper body. I also knew it would be tough sledding to accomplish this, because my upper body had exploded in growth. For example, my arms had increased from 17 inches to 20 inches in just over a year.

During the summer and fall when I was 18, I embarked on a specialized program of heavy leg training. I worked my calves hard, and I squatted until I was blue in the face. As a result of such training, my legs grew tremendously. Within a year they were perfectly proportioned to the rest of my body, and both my thighs and calves were ripped to shreds.

Bodybuilding history has shown how effective my thigh specialization workouts actually were. Within three years I had won Teenage Mr.

America, Mr. America, Mr. International, and Mr. Universe (twice). And had I not chosen to forego my competitive bodybuilding career to become television's Incredible Hulk, I'm sure I could have won the Mr. Olympia title while still in my mid-20s.

If your thigh development is lagging a little— or even if it isn't, but you simply wish to improve their size and muscularity—I'm sure that some of my thigh training secrets will benefit you. Thigh training is extremely hard work, but the rewards make the hard work worthwhile.

As proven by the Weider Overload Training Principle, there is a direct relationship between thigh strength and thigh development. The full Squat is the basic thigh exercise. And the heavier you squat for 5-6 reps (or more) per set, the greater will be your thigh development.

At the beginning and intermediate levels of training, the only exercise you probably need to do for your thighs is the Squat. Typically, a beginner can do three or four sets of 8-10 reps in the Squat. You will see results even if you use a constant weight for every set. But it is advisable to warm up by using a moderate weight for your

Hack Squat: start.

first set, then add 10–15 pounds to the bar for each succeeding set.

Intermediate-level bodybuilders should pyramid their sets and reps when squatting. Pyramidding means you decrease the reps and increase the training poundage with each succeeding set of an exercise. This is an excellent way to build both power and mass when doing a basic exercise for any body part. And pyramidding allows you to warm up thoroughly, do some midrange reps for shape and muscle quality, and finally get in some low-rep sets for mass and power.

Here's a typical pyramidding routine that an intermediate bodybuilder can use. The weights have been chosen arbitrarily and are intended only to show how poundages increase during a pyramid workout.

Set Number	Reps	Weight
1	12	135 lbs.
2	10	185
3	8	225
4	6	255
5	4	280
6	2–3	300

On this pyramidding program, you'll find that your strength and size will increase very quickly. In fact, you will be able to add 10 pounds to your squat each week for a year.

At the intermediate level of bodybuilding, you can begin doing Leg Curls to fill out your hamstrings. You can also do a few sets of Leg Extensions to shape and define your thighs. Eventually you should do the Leg Extensions at the beginning of your workout to thoroughly warm up your knees and thighs prior to doing heavy Squats.

Considering all of these suggestions for intermediate-level training, here is a good all-round thigh workout.

Exercise	Sets	Reps
1. Squat	6	12–2
2. Leg Extension	3–4	8–10
3. Leg Curls	4–5	8–10

This routine can be used steadily for one year.

Since my thighs were lagging so badly in my late teens, I had to embark on a super-concentrated, specialized thigh routine. I decided to train the thighs only in two of my workouts each week, and to work the rest of my body in my four other weekly training sessions. This was a variation of the Weider Muscle Priority Training Principle. And I resolved to concentrate on my Squats, persistently increasing my Squat weights by 10–20 pounds each week.

Here is the thigh workout I used so successfully when I was 18:

Exercise	Sets	Reps
1. Squat	6–8	15–2
2. Leg Press	4–5	12–4
3. Leg Extension	4–5	10–12
4. Leg Curl	6–8	10–12

This workout was effective for buildilng up my thighs. I still do a workout similar to this, although now I do fewer total sets, because my thighs are up to par with the rest of my body.

When a bodybuilder is preparing for a competition, he or she should do fewer Squats and more isolation movements to bring out maximum thigh cuts. Peak Contraction exercises become particularly important during contest preparation. And while I personally don't like them, many bodybuilders will superset (or even tri-set) their thigh exercises. Finally, most bodybuilders do many more sets prior to a contest than in the off-season.

Here is how I usually trained my thighs prior to a competition:

Exercise	Sets	Reps
1. Front Squat	5–6	10–15
2. Hack Squat	4–5	10–15
3. Leg Extension	4–5	10–15
4. Leg Curl	5–6	10–15
5. Lunges	3–4	10–15

This type of routine maintained my thigh mass while dramatically increasing my leg shape and definition.

Undeniably, developing a good pair of thighs takes discipline and determination. You'll leave plenty of sweat at the Squat rack in the process. But with consistent hard work, any male or female bodybuilder will be able to achieve excellent thigh development.

EXERCISE DESCRIPTIONS

Squat

This is the basic thigh movement. It boosts the body's metabolism and helps you gain lean muscle mass. Many bodybuilders call the Squat the "king of bodybuilding exercises."

Start with your feet set at about shoulder width, your toes angled outward at about 45 degrees on each side. Rest a heavy barbell behind your neck across your trapezius muscles and balance it in place with your hands. Stand erect and focus your gaze at shoulder level throughout the movement. This will keep your head up as you squat and prevent your back from rounding during the movement. Tense your back muscles and keep them tight for the whole set.

From this basic starting position, squat down until your thighs are below an imaginary line drawn parallel to the floor. As you squat down, your torso should be held as erect as possible, and your thighs should travel outward at 45-degree angles directly over the line of your feet. Do not bounce at the bottom of the movement. Simply stop the movement once your thighs are below parallel and then return to the starting point by straightening your thighs. Repeat the movement for the required number of repetitions.

You should wear a weightlifting belt when doing your Squats. If you experience difficulty doing your Squats flatfooted (a sign of ankle inflexibility), you can rest your heels on a 2 × 4–inch board while squatting.

Squats: start, above; finish, below.

Front Squats

This movement is very similar to squats, except that the bar is held across the upper chest and shoulders during the movement, rather than across the upper back and shoulders. Front Squats place more stress on the muscles just above the knees than do regular Squats.

Front Squat: finish.

Leg Press: start, above; finish, below.

Leg Press

Many bodybuilders use Leg Presses in place of Squats, because Leg Presses place less strain on the lower back. Start by lying with your head at the lower end of an angled board and your hips directly under the movable platform. Place your feet on the board at shoulder width and straighten your legs. Release the safety stops of the machine. Bend your legs as fully as possible, then straighten them. Repeat for the required number of repetitions.

Hack Squats

I've found this to be an excellent movement for enhancing thigh cuts and shape. Place your feet on the angled platform with your heels about 12 inches apart and your toes pointed outward at 45-degree angles on each side. Bend your legs fully and rest your back against the sliding platform. Grasp the handles beside your

hips to steady your back against the sliding platform. From this position, straighten and bend your legs for the required number of repetitions.

Lunges

This is a basic movement for enhancing definition, and it should be used prior to a competition. It is particularly good for improving your upper thigh muscularity. Start in the same position as you would for a regular Squat, but use a much lighter barbell. Step forward 2.5–3 feet with your left foot (your toes should be pointed directly forward). Keeping your right leg straight, fully bend your left knee. At the bottom position of the movement, your left knee should be 4–6 inches ahead of your left ankle, and your right knee should be 2–3 inches above the floor. Push hard with your left thigh muscles to return to the starting point. Do your next repetition with your right leg forward, and alternate legs for the full number of repetitions.

Leg Extensions

Sit at the end of a leg table so the backs of your knees are right against the edge of the pad. Hook the insteps of your feet under the lower set of roller pads. To keep your body in position during the movement, grasp the handles provided next to your hips, or the sides of the table. From this basic starting point, simply extend your legs slowly until they are completely straight. Hold this position for a count of two or three to assure that you have a peak contraction. Slowly lower back to the starting point and repeat the movement for the required number of repetitions.

Leg Curls

This is the best exercise for developing the hamstring muscles at the backs of your thighs. Lie facedown on the leg table so your knees are against the padded surface at the edge of the table. Hook your heels under the upper set of roller pads and fully straighten your legs. To steady your body in this position, grasp the handles beside and below your shoulders, or the edges of the table. Then slowly bend your legs as fully as possible. Hold this position two or three seconds for a peak contraction effect. Then lower back to the starting point. Repeat for the desired number of repetitions.

Leg Extensions: start, left; finish, below.

inches of each other. With your arms and hands in this position, you will really bring the outside or lateral head of the triceps out. Also, concentrate on the maximum stretch you can achieve with each repetition. I do three sets of 8–12 repetitions, resting only 15 seconds between sets.

To fully saturate the triceps-chest-deltoid area, I find weighted Parallel Bar Dips are without equal. I call these weighted dips "Power Dips," because I place most of the emphasis on the amount of weight I am able to handle. Use a medium-width set of parallel bars and perform four sets of 8–10 reps. Remember to fully lockout on each repetition and hold it for three seconds, tensing the triceps.

Bench Dips will put the finishing touches on

your triceps. Depending on your strength, you may or may not want to use additional weight (i.e., other than your body weight). Take a narrow grip with the hands almost together. Your feet should be at a higher elevation than your hands. Lower yourself slowly to the lowest position on each rep; also, extend and fully contract on each three-second lockout. Perform three sets of 15–20 reps. The extreme burn and pump you'll receive will tell you that you're on your way to building terrific triceps.

I've always been very proud of my triceps development, both in terms of size and definition. Building triceps like mine will be easier for you if you use the specific exercises and the iso-tension repetition technique I have described. Good luck.

"Nothing bulks up the triceps with solid muscle like Lying Triceps Extensions with an EZ-curl bar. Try to keep your elbows from traveling outward from the midline of your body during the movement."

"Weighted Parallel Bar Dips are an excellent triceps bulking movement as well as a good deltoid and pectoral exercise. Be sure to keep your torso upright throughout the movement."